KRYSIA AHMAD obtained her B.A. honours degree in the natural sciences, and later her M.A. degree, from the University of Cambridge. While at Cambridge she taught chemistry, physics and mathematics on a private tutorial basis. She has considerable experience of publishing, having edited many research journals and scientific publications. She has been involved in the Key Facts series in a scientific advisory capacity and is now a freelance writer and editor.

D0865861

Reference Library

BIOLOGY, R. Whitaker, B.Sc., and
J. M. Kelly, B.Sc.

MATHEMATICS, K. Ahmad, M.A.

PHYSICS, K. Ahmad, M.A.

Key Facts Reference Library

G.C.E. O-Level

CHEMISTRY

by Krysia Ahmad, M.A.

Published by Intercontinental Book Productions
in conjunction with Seymour Press Ltd.
Distributed by Seymour Press Ltd.,
334 Brixton Road, London, SW9 7AG

Published 1978 by Intercontinental Book Productions,
Berkshire House, Queen Street, Maidenhead, Berks., SL6 1NF
in conjunction with Seymour Press Ltd.

1st edition, 1st impression 8.78.1.
Copyright © 1978 Intercontinental Book Productions
Made and printed in England by C. Nicholls & Company Ltd
ISBN 0 85047 9185

Contents

Continued on page 6

Introduction

The book is intended both for students of O-level Chemistry, Chemistry with Physics and General Science and for students of related subjects who require a working knowledge of chemistry.

The book is designed to serve both as a quick and easy reference guide and as an aid to revision. The contents cover all the main topics and many minor ones listed by the various examining boards.

The subject material is divided into topics, each topic consisting of a list of statements, definitions and formulae. The entries are arranged in a logical subject order and not in alphabetical order. Each entry begins with the title in bold placed at the left-hand side of the page. A word, or words, appearing in bold in the body of the entry denote an important term or concept. Each entry has been written in a concise but easy to understand form with necessary details and explanations being given. The Periodic Table of Elements is given on pages 92 and 93.

The system of units and nomenclature adopted in the book follows the recommendations of the various Examination Boards and of the Association for Science Teaching. A list of some common and chemical names is given on page 90.

Students often experience difficulty in extracting and appreciating the essential elements of a concept or an experiment. It is hoped that this book, in presenting the material in a concise yet simple form, will help the student to not only increase his knowledge of basic facts but also his understanding of the core or essence of the subject.

Atomic and Molecular Theory

Atomic and molecular theory is concerned with the physical nature of the particles (atoms and molecules) constituting matter, the ratios in which they combine to form compounds and the ratios in which the atoms and molecules in the compound interact in a chemical reaction.

An atom is the smallest particle of an element which can take part in chemical action.

Dalton's atomic theory consisted essentially of the following ideas:
1. Matter is made up of small indivisible particles called atoms.
2. Atoms can neither be created nor destroyed.
3. The atoms of any one element are all exactly alike in every way and are different from the atoms of all other elements.
4. Chemical reactions take place between small whole numbers of atoms.

Dalton's theory led to certain conclusions which were embodied in the laws of combination by mass (the following four laws) which have been verified experimentally.

Law of conservation of mass (or indestructibility of matter) Matter can neither be created nor destroyed during the course of a chemical reaction.

The law may be restated in the following form:

The total mass of the products of a given chemical reaction is equal to the total mass of the reagents used in the reaction.

This law provides evidence for the second point of Dalton's atomic theory.

Law of constant composition (or definite proportions)
All pure samples of a given chemical compound always contain the same elements in the same proportions by mass no matter how they are made.

This provides evidence for the third point of Dalton's atomic theory.

Law of multiple proportions If two elements, A and B, combine to form more than one compound, then the different masses of B which combine with a fixed mass of A in these compounds are in a simple whole number ratio.

This law provides evidence for the fourth point of Dalton's atomic theory.

Law of reciprocal proportions If an element A combines to form compounds with several other elements, B, C, D, then the masses of B, C, D which combine with a fixed mass of A are the masses of B, C, D which combine with each other, or simple multiples of those masses.

This law provides evidence for the fourth point of Dalton's atomic theory.

The relative atomic mass (atomic weight) of an element is the mass of one atom of the element compared with the mass of one atom of hydrogen.

It is increasingly being defined in the following way:

The relative atomic mass (atomic weight) of an element is the mass of one atom of the element compared with the mass of one atom of $_6^{12}C$ (or carbon-12), arbitrarily assigned the value 12.000.

Molecular theory

A molecule is the smallest part of an element or compound which can normally exist separately.

The relative molecular mass (molecular weight) of an element or compound is the mass of one molecule of the element or compound compared with the mass of an atom of $_6^{12}C$ (carbon-12) which is arbitrarily assigned the value 12.000.

The atomicity of an element is the number of atoms contained in one molecule of the element.

A monatomic molecule contains one atom, e.g. He helium
A diatomic molecule contains two atoms, e.g. Cl_2 chlorine
A triatomic molecule contains three atoms, e.g. O_3 ozone
A polyatomic molecule contains many atoms, e.g. S_8 sulphur

For Boyle's law and Charles' law see p. 13.

Gay Lussac's law of gaseous combining volumes When gases react they do so in volumes which bear a simple ratio to one another, and to the volume of the product if gaseous, temperature and pressure remaining constant. For example:

1. Steam $\qquad 2H_2(g) + O_2(g) \rightarrow 2H_2O(g)$

2 volumes of hydrogen combine with 1 volume of oxygen to give 2 volumes of steam

2. Ammonia $\qquad 2NH_3(g) \rightarrow N_2(g) + 3H_2(g)$

2 volumes of ammonia decompose to give 1 volume of nitrogen and 3 volumes of hydrogen

Avogadro's law Equal volumes of all gases at the same temperature and pressure contain the same number of molecules.

The Avogadro number (constant), N_A, is the number of atoms of carbon in exactly 12.000 grammes of $_6^{12}C$. It is equal to 6.02×10^{23} and is the number of molecules contained in one mole of any gas.

The vapour density of a gas or vapour is the ratio of the mass of a given volume of the gas or vapour to the mass of the same volume of hydrogen at the same temperature and pressure.

$$\text{Vapour density of gas or vapour} = \frac{\text{Mass of 1 volume of gas or vapour}}{\text{Mass of 1 volume of hydrogen}}$$

Relative molecular mass (molecular weight) of a gas or vapour

$$= \frac{\text{Mass of 1 molecule of gas or vapour}}{\text{Mass of 1 atom of hydrogen}}$$

Relationship between vapour density and relative molecular mass of a gas or vapour

$$\text{Relative molecular mass of gas or vapour} = 2 \times \text{vapour density}$$

The mole is the amount of substance which contains as many particles as there are carbon atoms in 12.000 grammes of $_6^{12}C$ (i.e. the Avogadro number, 6.02×10^{23}).

The molar mass (or gramme-molecular mass, G.M.M.) of any gas is its relative molecular mass expressed in grammes.

The molar volume (or gramme-molecular volume, G.M.V.) of any gas is the volume occupied at s.t.p. by one mole of molecules (gramme–molecule) of the gas and is equal to 22.4 dm^3 at s.t.p.

The States of Matter

All materials are composed of matter which exists in three different states – solid, liquid and gas. A substance is chemically the same in each of these three states, and may be converted from one state to the other by the addition or removal of heat energy. The difference in the properties of the three states of matter is due to the difference in the manner in which the molecules are arranged and in their respective motions, a property dealt with by kinetic theory.

The three states of matter

Kinetic theory states that all molecules, whether they be in the solid, liquid or gaseous state, are in some kind of motion, whether it be vibrations about a fixed point or fast random movement in all directions. The kinetic theory enables various phenomena to be explained, e.g. melting, pressure of gases, conduction and diffusion.

Solid state The particles (atoms, molecules or ions) in a solid are so tightly packed, and the forces of attraction between them so strong, that free movement of the particles cannot take place. Thus the solid consists of an ordered geometrical array of particles each vibrating about a fixed position. Solids therefore have a fixed shape and volume and resist any force which tries to distort them.

The particles constituting a solid structure may be:
1. *Atoms*. Many non-metals form crystals consisting of large numbers of atoms bonded covalently, e.g. carbon.
2. *Molecules*. e.g. iodine forms solids in which molecules of the element are held together by weak van der Waal's forces.
3. *Ions*. e.g. the sodium chloride lattice consists of an ordered geometrical array of sodium ions (Na^+) and chloride ions (Cl^-).

Liquid state The particles in a liquid are in perpetual random motion. The forces of attraction between the particles cause them to remain close together although they are further apart than in a solid. The particles at the surface of the liquid are attracted inward by the mass of particles in the liquid below them giving rise to surface tension. Liquids have a definite volume but take the shape of the part of the container they occupy. They are more comprehensive than solids, less so than gases.

Gaseous state The particles in a gas are in continuous, rapid random motion. The forces of attraction between particles are very small and thus they are much freer to move and the distance between them is much greater than in a liquid or solid. Gases have no fixed volume and fill completely any space open to them. They are highly compressible.

Comparison of solids, liquids and gases

Property	Solid	Liquid	Gas
Particle motion	Slow vibrations about a fixed point	Moderate random movement	Fast random movement in all directions
Volume and shape	Definite volume and shape	Definite volume, takes shape of part of container occupied	No definite volume, takes the shape of the container
Density	High	Medium	Low

Conduction is the process by which heat is transferred through a solid by the particles of the solid.

If one end of a solid is heated the kinetic energy of the molecules in that area increases and they begin to vibrate more violently, hitting molecules adjacent to them. These in turn vibrate more strongly hitting their neighbouring molecules and so on.

Changes of state

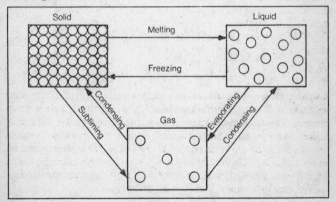

Figure 1. Interconversion of the three states of matter

11

Melting is the process which occurs when a substance changes from the solid state to the liquid state on heating. When a solid is heated, the particles (atoms, molecules, ions) acquire greater kinetic energy and begin to vibrate more strongly. Eventually a temperature is reached when the vibrations are sufficiently strong to overcome the forces of attraction between the particles. The crystalline structure then collapses to form the liquid state in which the particles are free to move.

The melting point, m.p., of a solid is the temperature at which the solid begins to liquefy. It is only slightly lowered by an increase in pressure; an impurity in the solid depresses the melting point and causes a gradual softening rather than a sharp liquefaction. A sharp melting at its accepted melting point is good evidence of purity in a solid.

Sublimation is the process which occurs when a substance changes from the solid state to the gaseous state without first passing to the liquid state. Iodine and ammonium chloride are examples of substances which sublime.

Evaporation of a liquid is the continuous process of molecules of liquid escaping from the surface of the liquid into the surrounding gaseous medium.
The particles at the surface of the liquid experience a net attractive force acting downwards. Some of the particles acquire sufficient kinetic energy to overcome these forces and escape from the surface of the liquid. The average kinetic energy of the remaining particles is decreased, thus evaporation lowers the temperature of the remaining liquid.

Boiling is the process which occurs when a substance changes from the liquid state to the gaseous state at a temperature at which the saturation vapour pressure of the liquid is equal to the atmospheric pressure.
As a liquid is heated the kinetic energy of the molecules increases. The rate of evaporation also increases which thus produces an increase in the vapour pressure of the liquid. When a temperature is reached at which the vapour pressure of the liquid equals the atmospheric pressure bubbles of vapour are able to form freely in the body of the liquid and rise to the surface. The liquid is then said to boil.

The boiling point, b.p., of a liquid is the temperature at which the vapour pressure of the liquid is equal to the atmospheric pressure. The boiling point is increased by an impurity or by increase in external pressure.

Gaseous state

Boyle's law The volume of a fixed mass of gas is inversely proportional to the pressure provided the temperature remains constant.

$$V \propto 1/P \qquad P_1 V_1 = P_2 V_2$$

According to kinetic theory as the volume of the gas decreases the average velocity of the gas molecules remains the same but the rate at which the gas molecules collide with the decreasing area of the walls of the containing vessel increases. The more frequent the collisions the higher the pressure.

Charles' law The volume of a fixed mass of gas is directly proportional to its absolute (kelvin) temperature provided the pressure remains constant.

$$V \propto T \qquad \frac{V_1}{T_1} = \frac{V_2}{T_2}$$

According to kinetic theory a fall in temperature produces a decrease in the average kinetic energy of the gas molecules and hence a decrease in molecular velocity. At constant pressure the decreased velocity causes the gas to occupy a smaller volume.

The ideal gas equation

$$\frac{P_1 V_1}{T_1} = \frac{P_2 V_2}{T_2}$$

The importance of the ideal gas equation is that it enables the volume of a fixed mass of gas, V_2, to be determined at any desired temperature T_2 and pressure P_2, provided its volume V_1 is known at a given temperature T_1 and pressure P_1.

An ideal (perfect) gas

Kinetic theory makes the following assumptions about an ideal gas:

1. Gas pressure is exerted in a vessel as a result of the collisions between the gas molecules and the walls of the container. The number of collisions in unit time being very great, the pressure appears constant (at constant temperature).

2. The total volume of the gas molecules is negligible compared with the volume of the container.

3. The forces of attraction and repulsion between gas molecules is negligible.

4. The average kinetic energy of the gas molecules measures the temperature of the gas.

Standard temperature and pressure (s.t.p.)

Since the volumes of gases change markedly with change in pressure and temperature it is necessary to adopt fixed values of these variables as standards to which gas volumes may be referred.

Standard temperature is 273 K (0 °C)

Standard pressure is 760 mm of mercury

Dalton's law of partial pressures The total pressure exerted by a mixture of gases which do not interact chemically is equal to the sum of the partial pressures of the constituent gases. In a mixture of gases the partial pressure of each gas is the pressure the gas would exert if it alone occupied the container at the same temperature and pressure.

Diffusion of a gas or liquid is the spreading of the substance owing to the spontaneous movement of its molecules from one place to another and is independent of gravity.

Graham's law of diffusion The rate of diffusion of a gas is inversely proportional to the square root of its density.

$$R \propto \frac{1}{\sqrt{D}} \quad \text{where} \quad \begin{aligned} R &= \text{rate} \\ D &= \text{density} \end{aligned} \quad \frac{R_1}{R_2} = \sqrt{\frac{D_2}{D_1}}$$

The density of a gas is proportional to its vapour density which in turn is proportional to its molecular weight, thus

$$\frac{R_1}{R_2} = \sqrt{\frac{M_2}{M_1}} \quad \text{where } M_1, M_2 \text{ are molecular weights}$$

Brownian movement is the irregular haphazard movement of small particles of solids, e.g. pollen grains, particles of tobacco smoke, suspended in a liquid or gas. It is caused by the bombardment on all sides of the solid particles by the particles of liquid and gas which are themselves in continuous random motion.

Elements, Compounds, Mixtures and Solutions

The number of substances which cannot be broken down into simpler substances (elements) is small compared with the number of substances which consist of two or more elements chemically combined and which may be broken down into the constituent elements by chemical means.

An element is a substance which cannot be split up into two or more simpler substances by any known chemical process.

A compound is a substance which contains two or more elements chemically combined together.

Examples of compounds and the elements they contain

Compound	Elements contained
Water	Hydrogen, Oxygen
Silver nitrate	Silver, Nitrogen, Oxygen
Common salt	Sodium, Chlorine
Sugar	Carbon, Hydrogen, Oxygen

A mixture consists of two or more substances, either compounds or elements, which are not combined together chemically.

Differences between mixtures and compounds

Mixtures	Compounds
1. A mixture can have any composition.	1. Compounds are fixed in their composition.
2. The constituents can be separated from each other by physical means.	2. The constituents can only be separated by chemical means.
3. The properties of a mixture are the sum of the properties of the constituents of the mixture.	3. The properties of a compound are unique and usually quite different from those of the constituent elements.
4. The preparation of a mixture does not usually involve any energy change.	4. The formation of compounds is usually accompanied by one or more energy changes. (e.g. heat)

Categories of mixtures

Mixtures can be divided into four main groups.

1. Mixtures of solids, e.g. salt and sugar.
2. Mixtures of solids and liquids, e.g. sea water.
3. Mixtures of liquids, e.g. petrol.
4. Mixtures of gases, e.g. air.

Separation of mixtures

1. *Mixture of solids*. By shaking with a liquid in which one of the components is soluble and the other insoluble. The insoluble component is separated from the solution by filtering the hot solution or by centrifuging and decanting the supernatant liquid. The soluble component can be recovered from the solution by crystallization or, in the case of a substance unaffected by heat, by evaporation to dryness by heating.

2. *Mixture of solid and liquid*
(i) *Solid insoluble in liquid*. By filtration. The insoluble component remains as residue on the filter paper; the liquid filtrate passes through the filter paper.
(ii) *Solid dissolved in liquid*. By evaporation, either slow evaporation (crystallization) or fast evaporation (evaporation to dryness) which is suitable for solids unaffected by heat.
(iii) Small amounts of solids may be separated by chromatography (see p. 18).

3. *Mixture of liquids*
(i) *Miscible liquids*. By fractional distillation. The liquid with the lowest boiling point distils first and is condensed, followed by the second liquid and so on.
(ii) *Immiscible liquids*. By separating funnel. The most dense liquid falls to the bottom.

4. *Mixture of gases*
(i) By absorption of one gas. The mixture is bubbled through a solution which selectively absorbs one of the gases.
(ii) By liquefying the mixture followed by fractional distillation.

Solutions

A solute is the substance which dissolves when a solution is made, e.g. salt is the solute in salt solution.

A solvent is a substance that causes dissolving to take place when a solution is made, e.g. salt (solute) dissolves in water (solvent).

A solution is formed when a solute dissolves in a solvent.

Solute + Solvent = Solution

A suspension consists of small particles of a solid contained in a liquid but not dissolved in it.

An alloy is a solid solution, compound or mixture of two or more metals, e.g. brass is an alloy of copper and zinc formed by dissolving zinc in copper to form a solid solution of zinc in copper.

A saturated solution at a given temperature is one in which no more solute will dissolve, crystals of the solute being present in the solution.
A saturated solution is said to be in equilibrium with the solid state.

The solubility of a substance in a solvent at a given temperature is the number of grammes of the substance that will dissolve in 100 grammes of the solvent in the presence of undissolved solid to form a saturated solution.

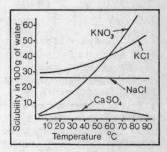

Figure 2. Solubility curves

Solubility curves A graph of the solubility of a substance against temperature. The solubility of most substances increases with temperature.

A super-saturated solution is one which contains more of the solute than the solution could hold at that temperature if crystals of the solute were present. Super-saturated solutions are unstable and if stirred or shaken or if dust particles contaminate the solution, crystals form immediately giving a true saturated solution.

Filtrate is the liquid free from the solids it contained, after passing the mixture through a filter.

Supernatant liquid is the clear liquid above a precipitate which has just settled out.

Crystallization is the slow formation of crystals from a melt or solution. The process is used to obtain soluble salts from their solutions.

Fractional crystallization is the process whereby a mixture of substances in solution is separated by the repeated partial crystallization of the solution.

17

Recrystallization is the process whereby impurities may be separated from the solid. The solid is dissolved in a suitable solvent and allowed to crystallize, the impurities being left in the solution.

The mother liquor is the liquid associated with crystals after crystallization has taken place. It is usually decanted, and the rest removed from the crystals by drying between filter papers.

Distillation is the process of heating a liquid in order to convert it to the gaseous state. The vapour is condensed and the condensed liquid (**distillate**) collected. Distillation is employed in the purification and separation of liquids and liquid mixtures, the liquid with the lowest boiling point being collected first (see Fig. 3).

Fractional distillation is the process of distillation using a fractionating column. This enables a better separation of liquids to be achieved than with the ordinary distillation apparatus.

A fractionating column consists of a column of glass containing flat discs or rings etc. which provide a much increased surface area for ascending vapour to condense on. As the column is ascended the concentration of the most volatile liquid in the vapour increases (see Fig. 3).

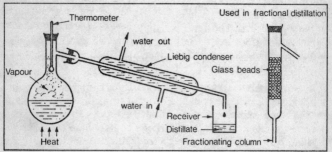

Figure 3.   Distillation apparatus and fractionating column

Chromatography is a method for separating or analyzing mixtures.

Adsorption chromatography depends on the fact that some solutions are more easily adsorbed by a solid adsorbent than others.

Paper chromatography. Here the liquid is drawn up a wick to the centre of the absorbent paper. It spreads out from the centre, the different substances in the liquid being absorbed at different rates, resulting in a chromatograph consisting of a series of concentric rings.

18

Formulae and Equations

Atomic symbols Atoms of elements are each represented by a symbol, e.g. sodium atom by Na, chlorine atom by Cl. The symbol represents one atom of the element. If the symbol consists of two letters the first letter is always a capital, the second letter always a small letter.

The molecular formula of a substance represents the actual number of atoms of each element present in one molecule of the substance, e.g. H_2SO_4 represents one molecule of sulphuric acid containing 2 atoms of hydrogen, 1 atom of sulphur and 4 atoms of oxygen.

A radical is a group of atoms which is found as a unit in many compounds but which does not normally have an independent existence, e.g. $-NO_3$ is the nitrate radical and is found in all nitrates.

The valency of an element is the number of hydrogen atoms one atom of the element will combine with or displace.
Similarly for radicals. Some elements have variable valency, in which case they form several different sets of compounds equal in number to the number of different valencies they possess.

Symbols and valencies of some common elements

Element	Symbol	Valency
Aluminium	Al	3
Bromine	Br	1
Calcium	Ca	2
Carbon	C	4
Chlorine	Cl	1
Copper	Cu	1 or 2
Hydrogen	H	1
Iodine	I	1
Iron	Fe	2 or 3
Lead	Pb	2 or 4
Magnesium	Mg	2
Oxygen	O	2
Potassium	K	1
Silver	Ag	1
Sodium	Na	1
Zinc	Zn	2

Symbols and valencies of some common radicals

Radical	Symbol	Valency
Ammonium	NH_4-	1
Carbonate	$-CO_3$	2
Chloride	$-Cl$	1
Hydrogencarbonate	$-HCO_3$	1
Hydrogensulphate	$-HSO_4$	1
Hydrogensulphite	$-HSO_3$	1
Hydroxide	$-OH$	1
Nitrate	$-NO_3$	1
Nitrite	$-NO_2$	1
Oxide	$-O^{2-}$	2
Phosphate	$-PO_4$	3
Sulphate	$-SO_4$	2
Sulphide	$-S$	2
Sulphite	$-SO_3$	2

Chemical equations are representations of chemical changes in symbols. Equations state:
1. the reactants and resultants.
2. the physical state of the reactants and resultants according to the **state symbols**
   (g) – gas, (l) – liquid, (aq) – aqueous solution, (s) – solid
3. the ratios of the reacting compounds
   e.g. $2NaOH(s) + H_2SO_4(aq) \rightarrow Na_2SO_4(aq) + 2H_2O(l)$
   2 mols + 1 mol   1 mol + 2 mols

Equations do not state the conditions of the reaction.

A balanced chemical equation is one in which the total number of atoms of each element on the left-hand side of the equation equals the total number of atoms of the element on the right-hand side. The number of molecules of reagents and re-sultants is altered until balance is achieved.

An ionic equation represents a chemical change in terms of the ions involved. Reduction–oxidation reactions are often represented in this way.

A balanced ionic equation is one in which:
1. the charges on each side are equal.
2. there is no net gain or loss in electrons.

$$2Na(s) - 2e \rightarrow 2Na^+(aq)$$
$$2H^+(aq) + 2e \rightarrow H_2(g)$$
$$\overline{2Na(s) + 2H^+(aq) \rightarrow 2Na^+(aq) + H_2(g)}$$

Atomic Structure and Bonding

The atom is made up of three fundamental particles – the electron, the proton and the neutron. The neutrons and protons are in the nucleus of the atom; the electrons circulate around the nucleus. Each element has a unique number of protons and of electrons, which determine its chemical behaviour. It is the electrons in the valency shell which interact when a chemical change takes place.

A proton is a positively charged particle found in the nucleus of the atom. It carries a charge of $+1$ and has a mass of 1 unit.

A neutron is a particle found in the nucleus of the atom. It is neutral (zero charge) and has a mass of 1.

An electron is a negatively charged particle in orbit around the nucleus. It carries a charge of -1 (equal and opposite to that on the proton) and has negligible mass.

Comparison of the proton, neutron and electron

Particle	Charge	Mass
Proton	$+1$	1
Neutron	0	1
Electron	-1	1/1840

The atomic number (proton number), Z, of an element is the number of protons in the nucleus of the atom. Since all atoms are electrically neutral it is also equal to the number of electrons in orbit around the nucleus.

Each element has a unique atomic number. The chemical behaviour of the element depends on its atomic number and not its atomic weight since it is the number and arrangement of electrons which determine chemical behaviour.

The mass number (nucleon number), A, of an element is equal to the number of protons plus the number of neutrons in the nucleus of the atom. Isotopic forms of an element have different mass numbers.

Examples of atomic numbers and mass numbers. An atom is represented by writing the mass number at the top L.H. of the chemical symbol and the atomic number at the bottom L.H. side.

Element	Symbol	Atomic number (Z)	Mass number (A)	Number of protons (Z)	Number of electrons (Z)	Number of neutrons (A − Z)
Hydrogen	$_1^1H$	1	1	1	1	0
Lithium	$_3^7Li$	3	7	3	3	4
Chlorine	$_{17}^{35}Cl$	17	35	17	17	18
(2 isotopes)	$_{17}^{37}Cl$	17	37	17	17	20

Electron distribution in the atom The electrons which revolve around the nucleus of an atom do so according to a definite pattern, details of which are summarized below:

1. The electrons form groups known as electron shells.
2. The electrons in any one shell maintain a definite average distance from the nucleus.
3. All electrons in any one shell have equal energy (approx.). The energy increases in successive shells outwards from the nucleus.
4. The shells are numbered 1, 2, 3 outward from the nucleus.
5. The maximum number of electrons in any one shell numbered n is $2n^2$, i.e. the number of electrons possible in successive shells is 2, 8, 18, 32 ... etc.
6. The maximum number of electrons permitted in the outermost shell of any atom is 8.

Electron configuration of the simplest 20 elements

Element	Number of protons	Number of electrons in shells 1 2	Element	Number of protons	Number of electrons in shells 1 2 3 4
hydrogen	1	1	sodium	11	2 8 1
helium	2	2	magnesium	12	2 8 2
lithium	3	2 1	aluminium	13	2 8 3
beryllium	4	2 2	silicon	14	2 8 4
boron	5	2 3	phosphorous	15	2 8 5
carbon	6	2 4	sulphur	16	2 8 6
nitrogen	7	2 5	chlorine	17	2 8 7
oxygen	8	2 6	argon	18	2 8 8
fluorine	9	2 7	potassium	19	2 8 8 1
neon	10	2 8	calcium	20	2 8 8 2

Electron shell: see electron distribution in the atom.

An octet (eight) or duplet (two) in the outer electron shell of an atom is an extremely stable electronic arrangement.

Isotopes. Atoms of the same element having the same number of protons in their nucleus but a different number of neutrons are known as isotopes. They have the same atomic number but a different mass number. Since it is the number and arrangement of orbiting electrons which determine the chemical properties of an element, isotopes do not have different chemical properties though their physical properties such as b.p., density vary.

Bonding

When elements combine to form compounds they undergo a rearrangement of their electronic configuration to achieve a stable octet of electrons in their outer valency shell (inert gas structure). This may be achieved either by the transfer of electrons (electrovalent bonding) or by the sharing of electrons (covalent bonding) depending upon the elements involved.

Electrovalent or ionic bonds are formed when a metallic element or group transfers one or more electrons from its outermost electron shell to the outer electron shell of a non-metallic element. The number of electrons lost by the metallic element or group is equal to the valency of the element or group. The metallic particles become positively charged, the non-metallic particles negatively charged, the charged particles being called ions.

In this way both ions attain the stable outer electron structure of a noble gas, i.e. a duplet or octet of electrons.

Example of electrovalent (ionic) bond formation

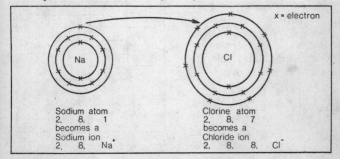

Figure 4.   Electron transfer to form an ionic bond

Comparison of the characteristic properties of electrovalent (ionic) and covalent compounds

Electrovalent (ionic) compounds	Covalent compounds
1. Ionic compounds do not contain molecules. They are crystalline solids consisting of aggregates of positively and negatively charged ions.	1. Usually volatile liquids or gases, existing as discrete molecules which may be held together by weak van der Waal's forces.
2. Usually have high melting and boiling points due to the forces of attraction between oppositely charged ions.	2. Usually have low melting and boiling points as the forces between molecules are weak.
3. Usually very soluble in water but only sparingly soluble in organic solvents.	3. Soluble in organic solvents but not usually soluble in water.
4. When molten (fused) they are good conductors of electricity because they are composed of ions.	4. Usually they are non-conductors of electricity.
Examples: All acids in solution, e.g. HCl, HNO_3; bases and alkalis, NaOH, salts, e.g. NaCl, KNO_3	*Examples:* Carbon dioxide, methane, ethene ethanol, carbon tetrachloride.

Sodium chloride lattice

Sodium chloride is a crystalline electrovalent solid consisting of oppositely charged particles (ions) of sodium (Na) and chlorine (Cl). Each ion of sodium is surrounded by six equi-distant chloride ions and vice versa.

An ion is an electrically charged atom or radical formed by the transfer of electrons. When an atom or radical loses electrons it forms a positively charged ion, when it gains electrons it forms a negatively charged ion.

Figure 5. Sodium chloride lattice

24

Electrovalence is the process of forming a compound by transfer of electrons.

An ionic pair consists of two oppositely charged ions held in close proximity by the strong electrostatic force between them.

Covalent bonds are formed by the sharing of electrons between the atoms concerned. Each atom contributes one electron for each covalent bond formed. In this way both atoms achieve a stable octet of electrons in their outer shell.

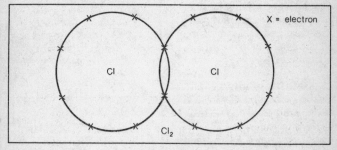

Figure 6. Electron sharing to form a covalent bond

Co-ordinate (dative) bond This is a type of covalent bond involving electron sharing but in which both electrons are supplied by the same atom. In this way both atoms achieve a stable octet structure in the outer shell. The atom donating the electron pair usually has a lone pair of electrons in the outer shell.

A lone pair of electrons Two electrons not directly concerned in the existing bonds formed within the compound, e.g. ammonia has a lone pair of electrons.

Metallic bond The atoms of metal are closely packed in a definite array and are held together by metallic bonds. The metallic atoms lose some of their outer electrons which form an electron cloud in random motion in the crystal lattice. The ions are closely packed, which accounts for the high densities of most metals compared with non-metals (Fig. 7).

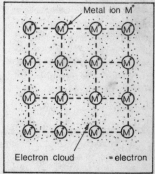

Figure 7. Metallic bonding

Shapes of molecules

Shape of carbon dioxide molecule The carbon atom is bonded to each oxygen atom by two pairs of electrons forming two covalent bonds. The electrons mutually repel each other producing a linear molecule (Fig. 8). In solid carbon dioxide (dry ice) the linear molecules take up a cubic formation, bonded by van der Waal forces.

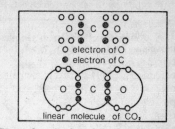

Figure 8. Carbon dioxide molecule

Shape of ammonia molecule The three hydrogen atoms are bonded covalently to the nitrogen atom. The nitrogen atom also has a lone pair of electrons not used in bonding. The mutual repulsion of the four electron pairs produces a triangular pyramidal shape of molecule (Fig. 9).

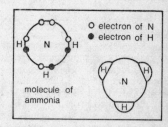

Figure 9. Ammonia molecule

Shape of steam (water) molecule The two hydrogen atoms are bonded covalently to the oxygen atom which has two lone pairs of electrons not used in bonding. The repulsion between the four pairs produces a structure in which the atomic nuclei all lie in the same plane (Fig. 10).

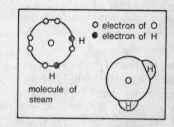

Figure 10. Steam (water) molecule

Allotropy is the ability of an element to exist in two or more distinct physical forms. It occurs when atoms of the same element are arranged in different ways, giving rise to differences in physical properties. Examples of allotropes are diamond and graphite, monoclinic and rhombic sulphur.

The Periodic Classification of the Elements

The Periodic Table The elements are arranged in order of increasing atomic number, a new horizontal row (period) beginning each time a new outer shell of electrons is started. The vertical columns (groups) consist of elements which have the same number of electrons in their respective outer shells and which therefore possess similar chemical properties. The chemical properties of an element are determined by the number and arrangement of electrons in orbit around the nucleus. Since the number of electrons is equal to the number of protons, the atomic mass of an element is a fundamental property.

Periods are the horizontal rows of elements in the Periodic table. All the elements in any one period have the same number of electron shells, e.g. silicon has the electronic arrangement 2, 8, 4, i.e. 3 shells of electrons and is hence found in Period 3.

Groups are the vertical columns of elements in the Periodic table. All elements in any one group have the same number of electrons in their outer shell and therefore possess similar chemical properties.

Variation in properties of elements along a period The electronegativity of elements increases along a period. For example, the first element in Period 2 is the highly electropositive element sodium, whereas the seventh element in Period 2 is the highly electronegative element chlorine. The reason for this is the increasing charge (number of protons) on the nucleus resulting in a strengthening of the forces holding the electrons in the outer shell.

Variation in properties of elements down a group The electropositive nature of elements increases down a group. The reason for this is the increase in size of the atom resulting in a weakening of the forces holding the electrons in the outer shell. This is shown by the increase in metallic properties on descending a group, e.g. in Group 5, the first element nitrogen is a gas, the last element is the metal bismuth.

Diagonal relationships The electronegativity of elements increases along a period and decreases down a group. As a result of this some elements which lie diagonally to each other possess very similar chemical properties.

Li   Be   B   C   lithium and magnesium

          ↘   ↘   ↘   beryllium and aluminium

Na Mg Al Si   boron and silicon

K   Ca Ga Ge

Families of elements

The vertical columns or groups in the Periodic table consist of elements which have similar properties and characteristics. These groups are therefore said to make up families of elements, e.g. alkali metals (Group 1), alkaline earth metals (Group 2).

Alkali metals are the elements comprising Group 1 (all have 1 electron in their outer shell) of the Periodic table, i.e. lithium, sodium, potassium, rubidium and francium. They are so called because when dissolved in water they form an alkaline solution. They are characterized by their reactivity with air and water, all members reacting spontaneously with air to form oxides. With water they react violently to give strong alkalis; the vigour of the reaction increases on descending the group.

Alkaline earth metals are the elements comprising Group 2 (all have 2 electrons in their outer shell) of the Periodic table, the first three being beryllium, magnesium and calcium.

Halogens are the elements comprising Group 7 of the Periodic table, i.e. fluorine, chlorine, bromine, iodine and astatine. They exhibit similar chemical properties owing to the fact that each element has seven electrons in the valency (outer) shell:
1. Strength of elements as oxidizing agents decreases in the order

$F \rightarrow Cl \rightarrow Br \rightarrow I$.

2. Steady gradation from F to I in the vigour of oxidation of hydrogen: fluorine combines explosively in the dark with hydrogen, chlorine slowly in daylight, bromine slowly in sunlight and iodine only on heating.

Inert (noble) gases are the elements comprising Group 8 of the Periodic table. They are helium, neon, argon, krypton, xenon and radon. All except helium possesses a completed outer shell of eight electrons, helium having a complete outer shell of two electrons. Because of this all are extremely stable and inert.

Types and Characteristics of Chemical Reactions

It is possible to distinguish between two kinds of changes – physical changes and chemical changes, each of which possesses distinct properties. Chemical changes can be further subdivided into types of reaction depending upon the phenomena associated with the reaction. Many reactions go to completion but there are a group of reactions, known as reversible reactions, which can proceed in either direction depending upon the reaction conditions. The rate of a chemical reaction depends upon several factors, the effects of which can often be explained on the basis of kinetic theory.

Differences between physical and chemical changes

Physical change	Chemical change
1. No new substance is formed	1. At least one new substance is formed
2. The change can often be easily reversed without requiring a chemical action	2. The change is usually very difficult and often impossible to reverse. A chemical action is always required to recover the original reagents
3. Usually only a small energy change is involved (except for changes of state which require latent heat)	3. A considerable energy change is often involved
4. There is no change in mass	4. There is no overall change in mass, but the mass of each product is different from the mass of any of the reactants
Examples of physical changes	Examples of chemical changes
1. The melting of a solid (or the reverse)	1. Burning any substance in air
2. The vaporization of a liquid (or the reverse)	2. Addition of sodium or potassium to water
3. Sublimation of iodine	3. Rusting of iron

Types of chemical reactions

Combination is the formation of a compound from two or more substances (elements or compounds), e.g.

$$Fe(s) + S(s) \rightarrow FeS(s)$$
$$CO(g) + \tfrac{1}{2}O_2(g) \rightarrow CO_2(g)$$

Synthesis is the formation of a compound from its *elements*. It may require more than one stage, e.g.

Synthesis of sulphuric acid:
$$\begin{cases} S(s) + O_2(g) \rightarrow SO_2(g) \\ SO_2(g) + \tfrac{1}{2}O_2(g) \rightarrow SO_3(g) \\ H_2(g) + \tfrac{1}{2}O_2(g) \rightarrow H_2O(l) \\ H_2O(l) + SO_3(g) \rightarrow H_2SO_4(aq) \end{cases}$$

Displacement is the reaction which occurs when one group (or element) takes the place of another group (or element) in a compound, e.g.

$$Zn(s) + CuSO_4(aq) \rightarrow ZnSO_4(aq) + Cu(s)$$
$$H_2S(g) + I_2(g) \rightarrow 2HI(g) + S(s)$$

Decomposition is the splitting up of a compound into simpler substances. The presence of a second substance is not usually necessary, the action of heat often being sufficient to make the reaction occur, e.g.

$$CaCO_3(s) \rightarrow CaO(s) + CO_2(g)$$
$$2NaNO_3(s) \rightarrow 2NaNO_2(s) + O_2(g)$$

Double decomposition is the reaction which occurs between two compounds which decompose and exchange radicals to form two new substances. The reactions are of the type:

$$A.B + C.D \rightarrow A.D + C.B$$

For example: $\quad Cu.SO_4(aq) + H_2.S(g) \rightarrow Cu.S(s) + H_2.SO_4(aq)$

Copper sulphide is insoluble and precipitates out. However, many reactions of double decomposition, particularly those taking place in an aqueous medium, are between compounds which are already fully ionised. The reaction does not involve decomposition of reactants. Simply that if ions present in the mixture can form an insoluble combination they will do so, the resulting compound precipitating out. For example, when a solution of sodium chloride (Na^+ and Cl^- ions) and a solution of silver nitrate (Ag^+ and NO_3^- ions) are mixed, silver chloride precipitates out leaving sodium nitrate (Na^+ and NO_3^- ions) in solution.

$$Ag^+(aq) + NO_3^-(aq) + Na^+(aq) + Cl^-(aq) \rightarrow$$
$$AgCl(s) + Na^+(aq) + NO_3^-(aq)$$

Thermal dissociation is the *reversible* splitting of a compound by the application of heat. On cooling the products recombine to form the original compound.

$$NH_4Cl(s) \rightleftharpoons NH_3(g) + HCl(g)$$
$$N_2O_4(g) \rightleftharpoons 2NO_2(g)$$

Thermal decomposition is the *irreversible* splitting of a compound by the application of heat. On cooling the products do not recombine to form the original compound.

$$NH_4NO_2(s) \rightarrow N_2(g) + 2H_2O(g)$$
$$2KClO_3(s) \rightarrow 2KCl(s) + 3O_2(g)$$

Reversible reactions and equilibrium

A reversible reaction is one which can proceed in either direction depending upon the experimental conditions.

$$CaCO_3(s) \rightleftharpoons CaO(s) + CO_2(g)$$
$$3Fe(s) + 4H_2O(g) \rightleftharpoons Fe_3O_4(s) + 4H_2(g)$$

Dynamic equilibrium In a reversible reaction the forward and backward reactions are proceeding simultaneously. After a time the concentrations of reactants and products remains constant provided the reaction conditions are unaltered. When this happens the rate of the forward reaction is equal to the rate of the backward reaction and the system is said to be in dynamic equilibrium.

Le Chatelier's Principle If a system in physical or chemical equilibrium has that equilibrium disturbed by a change in the temperature, pressure or concentration of reactants taking part, the equilibrium moves so as to oppose the effect of the change.

Factors affecting the position of equilibrium
1. *Temperature*

Nature of forward reaction	Change in temperature	Effect on equilibrium position of reaction $A + B \rightleftharpoons C + D$
Exothermic, e.g. $H_2(g) + I_2(g) \rightleftharpoons 2HI(g)$	increase	equilibrium moves to the left, i.e. more A and B formed
	decrease	equilibrium moves to the right, i.e. more C and D formed
Endothermic, e.g. $H_2O(l) \rightleftharpoons H_2O(g)$	increase	equilibrium moves to the right, i.e. more C and D formed
	decrease	equilibrium moves to the left, i.e. more A and B formed

2. *Pressure.* A change in pressure only produces a noticeable effect on the equilibrium position in gaseous reactions.

Type of reaction	Change in pressure	Effect of pressure change on equilibrium position
No change in volume, e.g. $H_2(g) + Cl_2(g) \rightleftharpoons$ $2HCl(g)$	increase	equilibrium position remains unchanged
	decrease	equilibrium position remains unchanged
Decrease in volume, e.g. $N_2(g) + 3H_2(g) \rightleftharpoons$ $2NH_3(g)$	increase	equilibrium moves to the right
	decrease	equilibrium moves to the left
Increase in volume, e.g. $N_2O_4(g) \rightleftharpoons$ $2NO_2(g)$	increase	equilibrium moves to the left
	decrease	equilibrium moves to the right

3. *Concentration.* If the concentration of one of the substances present in an equilibrium mixture is increased then, by Le Chatelier's principle, the position of equilibrium will move to decrease the concentration of the added substance.

Energy changes in chemical reactions

An exothermic reaction is one in which heat is liberated to the surroundings.

In an exothermic reaction the total energy of the products is less than the total energy of the reactants, the difference being equal to the amount of energy evolved in the form of heat. ΔH (which represents the energy change in a reaction, see p. 33) is negative for an exothermic reaction.

$$H_2(g) + \tfrac{1}{2}O_2(g) \rightarrow H_2O(l) \qquad \Delta H = -286 \text{ kJ}$$

An exothermic compound is one which is formed from its elements with the evolution of heat.

Exothermic compounds, e.g. hydrogen chloride, carbon monoxide and water, are usually very stable and not easily decomposed.

An endothermic reaction is one in which heat is absorbed from the surroundings.

In an endothermic reaction the total energy of the products is greater than the total energy of the reactants, the difference being equal to the amount of heat absorbed in the reaction. ΔH is positive for an endothermic reaction, e.g.

$$C(s) + H_2O(g) \rightarrow CO(g) + H_2(g) \qquad \Delta H = +131 \text{ kJ}$$

An endothermic compound is one which is formed from its elements with the absorption of heat. Endothermic compounds, e.g. acetylene, ozone tend to be unstable and decompose readily.

ΔH notation ΔH represents the heat change in a reaction, Δ = change in. (Unit: kJ.) ΔH is negative for an exothermic reaction and positive for an endothermic reaction. The magnitude of ΔH corresponds to the mole quantities of reactants as expressed in the equations for the reactions, e.g.

$$C(s) + 2S(s) \rightarrow CS_2(l) \qquad \Delta H = +117 \, kJ$$

Interpretation: When one mole of solid carbon reacts with two moles of solid sulphur to produce one mole of liquid carbon disulphide, 117 kJ of heat are absorbed from the surroundings.

Standard conditions for energy changes The value of an energy change, ΔH, for a reaction will vary depending upon (1) the physical state of the substances involved, (2) the temperature at which the measurement is made, (3) the pressure upon the system (only for gaseous reactions).

For this reason it is necessary to define a set of Standard conditions to allow comparisons of ΔH for different reactions.

> Standard temperature = 298 K (25 °C)
> Standard pressure   = 1 atmosphere

An energy change measured under Standard conditions is given the symbol $H^{\ominus}$.

The heat of combustion of a substance is the heat change which takes place when one mole of the substance is completely burned in oxygen.

The heat of neutralization of an acid or a base is the heat evolved when the amount of acid or base needed to form one mole of water is neutralized.

Essentially the heat of neutralization is the energy change for the reaction:

$$H^+(aq) + OH^-(aq) \rightarrow H_2O(l)$$
(from acid) (from base)

Law of conservation of energy Energy can neither be created nor destroyed; it can only be changed from one form into another form. This means that during any physical or chemical change the total energy of the reactants must equal the total energy of the products allowing for any energy (in the form of heat, light etc.) liberated to or absorbed from the surroundings.

Rate of reaction

The rate of a chemical reaction is the amount of reaction in unit time.

Activation energy Many reactions require a certain minimum energy to be supplied to them before they will start. This minimum or initiation energy is called activation energy.

Factors affecting Reaction Rate

1. *Concentration of reactants*. Increasing the concentration of any or all the reactants increases the reaction rate. According to kinetic theory reaction rate increases with increase in the frequency of collisions between reacting molecules. The greater the concentration of reactants the less the distance between reacting molecules and the greater the collision frequency.

2. *Temperature*. Increasing the temperature increases the rate of reaction in two ways: (a) the heat energy is converted into increased kinetic energy of the molecules which therefore move faster and collide more frequently, (b) the collisions between molecules are more energetic increasing the possibility of the activation energy being equalled or exceeded.

3. *Light* is a form of energy which increases the rate of some reactions, known as **photochemical** reactions. For example, a mixture of hydrogen and chlorine reacts very slowly in the dark or daylight but reacts explosively in sunlight. The light has sufficient energy to break the chlorine—chlorine bond and produce chlorine atoms which then react with the hydrogen.

$$Cl_2(g) \xrightarrow{light} Cl\cdot(g) + Cl\cdot(g)$$
$$Cl\cdot(g) + H_2(g) \rightarrow HCl(g) + H\cdot(g)$$
$$H\cdot(g) + Cl_2(g) \rightarrow HCl(g) + Cl\cdot(g) \text{ etc.}$$

4. *Surface area of reactants*. In a heterogeneous reaction in which all the reactants are not in the same phase, increasing the surface area of reactants increases the rate of reaction.

5. *A catalyst*, carefully chosen for the reaction, can greatly increase the reaction rate (see Catalysis on p. 35).

In summary, the rate of a reaction can be increased by:
1. Increasing the concentration of the reactants (for gaseous reactions increasing the total pressure of the system).
2. Increasing the temperature.
3. Increasing the amount of light for photochemical reactions.
4. Increasing the surface area of reactants.
5. A suitable catalyst.

Catalysis

Catalysis occurs when the rate of a chemical reaction is altered by an agent (the catalyst) which remains chemically unchanged at the end of the reaction.

A catalyst is a substance which alters the rate of a chemical reaction without itself being changed in mass or chemical composition during the course of the reaction.

A positive catalyst is one which increases the rate of a chemical reaction.

A negative catalyst or **inhibitor** is one which decreases the rate of a chemical reaction.

Features of catalytic action

1. The physical state of a catalyst may be altered during the course of a reaction.
2. Catalysts are usually only required in relatively small quantities.
3. Most catalysts are specific in their action, catalysing only one type of reaction.
4. In a reversible reaction a catalyst influences the rate of the forward and backward reactions to the same extent. It does not affect the equilibrium position but enables the equilibrium to be achieved more rapidly.

Examples of Catalysis

Reaction	Catalyst
1. Synthesis of ammonia (Haber process) $N_2(g) + 3H_2(g) \rightleftharpoons 2NH_3(g)$	Reduced iron (powder)
2. Heating of potassium chlorate $2KClO_3(s) \rightarrow 2KCl(s) + 3O_2(g)$	Manganese(IV) oxide MnO_2
3. Synthesis of sulphur trioxide $2SO_2(g) + O_2(g) \rightleftharpoons 2SO_3(g)$	Vanadium(V) oxide V_2O_5 or platinum (powder)

Oxidation and Reduction in terms of electron transfer

Oxidation is the process of electron loss.

Reduction is the process of electron gain.

An oxidizing agent is an acceptor of electrons.

A reducing agent is a donor of electrons.

The Electrochemical Series and Electrolysis

The electrochemical or reactivity series (electro-motive series)

A metal is an **electropositive element** since it ionizes to produce a positively charged ion. The electrochemical series is a list of metals placed in decreasing order of ease of ionization, i.e. decreasing order of electropositivity. Generally the more electropositive an element the more reactive it is, thus the metals occur in decreasing order of reactivity.

Potassium	K	↑	↑
Sodium	Na		
Calcium	Ca		
Magnesium	Mg		
Aluminium	Al		
Zinc	Zn	increasing	
Iron	Fe	ease of	increasing
Lead	Pb	ionization	reactivity
Hydrogen	H		
Copper	Cu		
Silver	Ag		
Gold	Au		

In general the properties of the elements and their compounds correspond to the position of the element in the electrochemical series as illustrated below.

Gradation in reactivity of elements on descending the Electrochemical Series

1. *Action with oxygen.* Potassium and sodium tarnish immediately when exposed to the air, each forming oxides. Calcium and magnesium will burn readily in air or oxygen while aluminium, zinc and iron require strong heat. Lead and copper oxidize when heated strongly but do not burn. Silver and gold form oxides with very great difficulty.
2. *Displacement of a metal by another metal.* A metal tends to displace another metal lower down in the series from a solution of its salt. The further apart the two metals in the series the greater the ease of displacement.

3. *Displacement of hydrogen from water*. Potassium, sodium and calcium all react with cold water to form the hydroxide and hydrogen,

e.g. $2Na(s) + 2H_2O(l) \rightarrow 2NaOH(aq) + H_2(g)$

Magnesium, aluminium, zinc and iron react very slowly with hot water. They react much more quickly with steam to form basic oxides,

e.g. $Mg(s) + H_2O(g) \rightarrow MgO(s) + H_2(g)$

The metals below iron do not react with water or steam.

4. *Displacement of hydrogen from dilute acid*. All metals which are more electropositive than hydrogen will displace hydrogen from acid,

e.g. $Zn(s) + H_2SO_4(aq) \rightarrow ZnSO_4(aq) + H_2(g)$

5. *Discharge of ions during electrolysis*. In general, if conditions are constant, positive ions tend to discharge at a cathode during electrolysis in reverse order of the electrochemical series, i.e. the least electropositive ion discharges first.

6. *Action of heat on compounds of metals*. The more electropositive a metal, the more stable a compound it tends to form, as illustrated in the table below:

Metal	Oxides	Nitrates	Carbonates
Potassium Sodium Calcium		Decompose to give nitrite and oxygen, e.g. $2NaNO_3(s) \rightarrow$ $\qquad 2NaNO_2(s) + O_2(g)$	Do not decompose unless very strongly heated
Magnesium Aluminium Zinc Iron Lead Copper	Do not decompose when heated	Decompose to give oxide, nitrogen dioxide and oxygen, e.g. $2Cu(NO_3)_2(s) \rightarrow$ $2CuO(s) + 4NO_2(g) + O_2(g)$	Decompose to give oxide and carbon dioxide, e.g. $CuCO_3(s) \rightarrow$ $\qquad CuO(s) + CO_2(g)$
Mercury Silver Gold	Decomposes to metal and oxygen, e.g. $2HgO(s) \rightarrow$ $2Hg(l) + O_2(g)$	Decompose to metal, nitrogen dioxide and oxygen, e.g. $Hg(NO_3)_2(s) \rightarrow$ $Hg(l) + 2NO_2(g) + O_2(g)$	Decompose to metal, oxygen and carbon dioxide, e.g. $2HgCO_3(s) \rightarrow$ $2Hg(l) + O_2(g) + 2CO_2(g)$

Electrolysis

Electrolysis is the decomposition of a compound, either molten or in solution, by means of passing an electric current through it.

An electrolyte is a compound which conducts electricity either in the fused state or in solution by the transfer of ions.

A non-electrolyte is a compound which is unable to ionize and cannot therefore conduct electricity.

An electrode is the conductor by which the electric current enters or leaves the electrolyte.

The cathode is the negative electrode by which the electrons enter the electrolyte.

The anode is the positive electrode by which the electrons leave the electrolyte.

An ion is formed when an atom or group of atoms loses or gains one or more electrons.

A cation is formed when an atom or a group of atoms loses one or more electrons; it migrates towards the cathode in electrolysis.

An anion is formed when an atom or a group of atoms gains one or more electrons; it migrates toward the anode in electrolysis.

Mechanism of electrolysis The positively charged ions (cations) are attracted toward the negative electrode, the cathode. On striking the cathode the ions acquire free electrons from the cathode to make them electrically neutral. The negatively charged ions (anions) are attracted toward the positive electrode, the anode. On striking the anode the ions lose electrons to make them electrically neutral. See examples on following pages.

Factors affecting the discharge of ions
1. The position of the ion in the electrochemical series.

Cations K^+ Na^+ Ca^{2+} Mg^{2+} Zn^{2+} Fe^{2+} Pb^{2+} H^+ Cu^{2+} Ag^+

Anions SO_4^{2-} NO_3^- Cl^- Br^- I^- OH^-

discharged last ⟵————————discharged first

2. The concentration of ions. If one ion has a much greater concentration than the others, despite its position in the series it may be preferentially discharged.
3. The type of electrodes. Inert electrodes, e.g. C or Pt, do not affect the ions discharged but others may do so.

Electrolysis of dilute sulphuric acid (acidified water)

Electrodes: platinum or carbon
Ions: From sulphuric acid $H^+(aq)$ $SO_4^{2-}(aq)$
From water $H^+(aq)$ $OH^-(aq)$

At cathode $(-)$
Ions present:
$H^+(aq)$
Ion discharge:
$2H^+(aq) + 2e \rightarrow H_2(g)$

Hydrogen is liberated
(2 volumes)

At anode $(+)$
Ions present:
$OH^-(aq)$ $SO_4^{2-}(aq)$
Ion discharge:
$4OH^-(aq) - 4e \rightarrow 2H_2O(l) + O_2(g)$

Oxygen is liberated
(1 volume)

Electrolysis of sodium hydroxide (caustic soda) solution

Electrodes: platinum
Ions: From sodium hydroxide $Na^+(aq)$ $OH^-(aq)$
From water $H^+(aq)$ $OH^-(aq)$

At cathode $(-)$
Ions present:
$Na^+(aq)$ $H^+(aq)$
Ion discharge:
$2H^+(aq) + 2e \rightarrow H_2(g)$

Hydrogen is liberated
(2 volumes)

At anode $(+)$
Ions present:
$OH^-(aq)$
Ion discharge:
$4OH^-(aq) - 4e \rightarrow 2H_2O(l) + O_2(g)$

Oxygen is liberated
(1 volume)

Electrolysis of copper(II) sulphate solution

(a) *Electrodes:* platinum or carbon
Ions: From copper(II) sulphate $Cu^{2+}(aq)$ $SO_4^{2-}(aq)$
From water $H^+(aq)$ $OH^-(aq)$

At cathode $(-)$
Ions present:
$Cu^{2+}(aq)$ $H^+(aq)$
Ion discharge:
$Cu^{2+}(aq) + 2e \rightarrow Cu(s)$

Copper is deposited

At anode $(+)$
Ions present:
$SO_4^{2-}(aq)$ $OH^-(aq)$
Ion discharge:
$4OH^-(aq) - 4e \rightarrow 2H_2O(l) + O_2(g)$

Oxygen is liberated

(b) *Electrodes:* copper
Ions: From copper sulphate $Cu^{2+}(aq)$ $SO_4^{2-}(aq)$
From water $H^+(aq)$ $OH^-(aq)$

At cathode $(-)$	At anode $(+)$
Ions present:	Ions present:
$Cu^{2+}(aq)$ $H^+(aq)$	$SO_4{}^{2-}(aq)$ $OH^-(aq)$
Ion discharge:	Ion discharge: $SO_4{}^{2-}$, OH^- are
$Cu^{2+}(aq) + 2e \rightarrow Cu(s)$	not discharged; the anode goes
Copper is deposited	into solution as $Cu^{2+}(aq)$ (re-
	quires less energy) $Cu(s) - 2e \rightarrow$
	$Cu^{2+}(aq)$

The cathode gains in weight, the anode loses weight.

Electrolysis of sodium chloride solution

Electrodes: Cathode may be platinum or carbon. Anode must be made of carbon to resist attack by chlorine.

Ions: From sodium chloride	$Na^+(aq)$ $Cl^-(aq)$
From water	$H^+(aq)$ $OH^-(aq)$

At cathode $(-)$	At anode $(+)$
Ions present:	Ions present:
$Na^+(aq)$ $H^+(aq)$	$Cl^-(aq)$ $OH^-(aq)$
Ion discharge:	Ion discharge:
$2H^+(aq) + 2e \rightarrow H_2(g)$	$2Cl^-(aq) - 2e \rightarrow Cl_2(g)$
Hydrogen is liberated	Chlorine is liberated
(1 volume)	(1 volume)

A cell converts chemical energy into electrical energy.

A primary cell is one in which the chemical energy of the constituents is converted into electrical energy when current is allowed to flow.

A secondary cell can be charged and discharged. On charge, when a current is passed through the cell, electrical energy is converted to chemical energy; on discharge the reverse takes place.

The Leclanché cell is a form of "primary cell". The cathode is a zinc rod or sheet, the anode a carbon rod, both of which are immersed in the electrolyte, ammonium chloride solution.

At cathode	At anode
$Zn(s) \rightarrow Zn^{2+}(aq) + 2e$	$2NH_4{}^+(aq) + 2e \rightarrow 2NH_3(g) + H_2(g)$

The carbon anode is immersed in a porous pot containing manganese(IV) oxide to oxidize the hydrogen and stop hydrogen bubbles adhering to the anode which would polarize the cell.

The lead accumulator is a secondary cell. The cathode and anode are grids of lead-antimony alloy. The electrolyte is dilute sulphuric acid. At discharge both grids carry a filling of lead sulphate.

During charge, in which direct current is passed through the cell, the following changes occur:

At cathode

$Pb^{2+}(aq) + 2e \rightarrow Pb(s)$

SO_4^{2-} goes into solution

At anode

$Pb^{2+}(aq) + 2H_2O(l) - 2e \rightarrow$
$\qquad\qquad PbO_2(s) + 4H^+(aq)$

SO_4^{2-} goes into solution

Thus, the cathode grid acquires a filling of spongy lead, the anode grid a filling of lead(IV) oxide. The concentration of the acid increases due to the passage of SO_4^{2-} and H^+ ions into solution. At full charge the e.m.f. is just above 2 volts.

During discharge the cell produces electrical energy by the following changes:

At cathode

$Pb(s) \rightarrow Pb^{2+}(aq) + 2e$

$Pb^{2+}(aq) + SO_4^{2-} \rightarrow PbSO_4(s)$
    from   deposited
    solution

At anode

$PbO_2(s) + 4H^+(aq) + 2e \rightarrow$
$\qquad\qquad Pb^{2+}(aq) + 2H_2O(l)$

$Pb^{2+}(aq) + SO_4^{2-}(aq) \rightarrow PbSO_4(s)$
      from   deposited
    solution

Electrons deposited on the cathode by ionization of lead move round the external circuit, performing useful work and are absorbed at the anode. The concentration of the acid decreases. The e.m.f. falls to a steady 2 volts and then to 1.8 volts, at which point it requires recharging.

Faraday's Laws of Electrolysis

1. *First law*. The mass of a substance liberated at (or dissolved from) an electrode during electrolysis is directly proportional to the quantity of electricity passing through the electrolyte.

$$\text{mass } (m) \propto \text{current } (I) \times \text{time } (t)$$

2. *Second law*. When the same quantity of electricity is passed through different electrolytes the number of moles of an element deposited is inversely proportional to the valency of the ion (which equals the charge on the ion).

This means that when one Faraday of electricity (see below) is used one mole of monovalent ions is liberated, or half a mole of divalent ions or a third of a mole of trivalent ions.

A Faraday is the quantity of electricity required in electrolysis to liberate 1 mole of monovalent ions, i.e. one Faraday is equal to one mole of electrons or the quantity of electricity which would be carried by the Avogadro number of electrons (6.02×10^{23}).

41

Acids, Bases and Salts

Acids

An acid is a compound which, when dissolved in water, produces hydrogen ions, $H^+(aq)$, as the only positive ion.

Examples: Hydrochloric acid $HCl \rightleftharpoons H^+ + Cl^-$
  Sulphuric acid $H_2SO_4 \rightleftharpoons 2H^+ + SO_4^{2-}$
  Nitric acid $HNO_3 \rightleftharpoons H^+ + NO_3^-$

The hydrogen ion is hydrated to the **hydroxonium ion**, H_3O^+,

$$\text{e.g.}\quad H_2O + HCl \rightleftharpoons H_3O^+ + Cl^-$$
$$2H_2O + H_2SO_4 \rightleftharpoons 2H_3O^+ + SO_4^{2-}$$

For most purposes the hydration of H^+ may be ignored.

A strong acid (in a given set of conditions) is one which in those conditions is highly ionized, e.g. in dilute (aqueous) solution, hydrochloric acid and sulphuric acid are almost 100% dissociated into ions and are therefore strong acids.

A weak acid (in a given set of conditions) is one which in those conditions is only slightly ionized, e.g. molar ethanoic acid is only 0.4% ionized and is therefore a weak acid.

$$CH_3COOH \rightleftharpoons CH_3COO^- + H^+$$

The strength of a weak acid increases as it becomes more dilute because its degree of dissociation into ions increases, i.e. the equilibrium in the above equation moves to the right.

The basicity of an acid is the number of hydrogen ions, $H^+(aq)$, which can be produced by one molecule of the acid.

Acid		Basicity
Nitric acid	$HNO_3 \rightleftharpoons H^+ + NO_3^-$	Monobasic
Ethanoic (acetic) acid	$CH_3COOH \rightleftharpoons CH_3COO^- + H^+$	Monobasic
Sulphuric acid	$H_2SO_4 \rightleftharpoons 2H^+ + SO_4^{2-}$	Dibasic
Phosphoric acid	$H_3PO_4 \rightleftharpoons 3H^+ + PO_4^{3-}$	Tribasic

Note that the basicity of an acid is not necessarily equal to the number of hydrogen atoms in the molecule. For example, acetic acid is monobasic although one molecule contains four atoms of hydrogen. Three of the hydrogen atoms are combined in such a way that they are unable to ionize.

Properties of acids

1. *Taste.* Many of the dilute acids have a sour taste.

2. *Action of litmus.* Most acids turn blue litmus red. Some of the weaker acids, e.g. carbonic acid, can only turn it to claret colour.

3. *Action with metals.* Metals which are much more electropositive than hydrogen (see p. 52) react with dilute hydrochloric acid/or dilute sulphuric acid with the liberation of hydrogen.

$$Zn(s) + H_2SO_4(aq) \rightarrow ZnSO_4(aq) + H_2(g)$$
$$Zn(s) + 2H^+(aq) \rightarrow Zn^{2+}(aq) + H_2(g)$$

Nitric acid is too strong an oxidizing agent to allow the liberation of hydrogen. It reacts with most metals to give oxides of nitrogen. Hydrogen is only obtained when magnesium reacts with the very dilute acid.

4. *Action with carbonates.* Acids liberate carbon dioxide from carbonates and hydrogencarbonates.

$$Na_2CO_3(s) + 2HCl(aq) \rightarrow 2NaCl(aq) + H_2O(l) + CO_2(g)$$
$$CO_3^{2-}(s) + 2H^+(aq) \rightarrow H_2O(l) + CO_2(g)$$

5. *Action with bases and alkalis.* Acids are neutralized by bases (basic oxides and hydroxides) and alkalis to form a salt and water.

$$CuO(s) + H_2SO_4(aq) \rightarrow CuSO_4(aq) + H_2O(l)$$
$$KOH(aq) + HCl(aq) \rightarrow KCl(aq) + H_2O(l)$$
$$H^+(aq) + OH^-(aq) \rightarrow H_2O(l)$$

Preparation of acids

1. By dissolving the acidic oxide of a non-metal (acid anhydride) in water.

Examples are the preparation of:

Sulphurous acid $\quad SO_2(g) + H_2O(l) \rightarrow H_2SO_3(aq)$

Sulphuric acid $\quad SO_3(g) + H_2O(l) \rightarrow H_2SO_4(aq)$

Metaphosphoric acid $\quad P_4O_{10}(s) + 2H_2O(l) \rightarrow 4HPO_3(aq)$

2. By displacing a weaker or more volatile acid from its salt with a stronger or less volatile acid.

Examples are the preparation of:

Hydrogen chloride $NaCl(s) + H_2SO_4(aq) \rightarrow$
$$NaHSO_4(aq) + HCl(g)$$

Nitric acid $\quad 2NaNO_3(s) + H_2SO_4(aq) \rightarrow$
$$Na_2SO_4(aq) + 2HNO_3(aq)$$

Boric acid $\quad Na_2B_4O_7(s) + H_2SO_4(aq) + 5H_2O(l) \rightarrow$
borax
$$Na_2SO_4(aq) + 4H_3BO_3(aq)$$
boric acid

3. By precipitating an insoluble sulphide from a solution of a metallic salt using hydrogen sulphide.

For example preparation of:

Ethanoic acid

$$Pb(C_2H_3O_2)_2(aq) + H_2S(g) \rightarrow PbS(s) + 2CH_3COOH(aq)$$

Bases and alkalis

A base is a substance which can combine with hydrogen ion, $H^+(aq)$. An alternative definition is:

A base is a substance which will react with an acid to form a salt and water.

Bases are usually ions, examples of which are given below:

Base	Base	Acid	Strength of base
Nitrate ion	$NO_3^- + H^+$	$\rightarrow HNO_3$	very weak
Sulphate ion	$SO_4^{2-} + 2H^+$	$\rightarrow H_2SO_4$	very weak
Chloride ion	$Cl^- + H^+$	$\rightarrow HCl$	very weak
Carbonate ion	$CO_3^{2-} + 2H^+$	$\rightarrow H_2CO_3$	strong
Ethanoate ion	$CH_3COO^- + H^+$	$\rightarrow CH_3COOH$	strong
Hydroxyl ion	$OH^- + H^+$	$\rightarrow H_2O$	very strong

Strength of base. If the equilibrium in the above equations lies markedly to the left the base is said to be weak; if the equilibrium lies markedly to the right the base is said to be strong.

Bases are subdivided into basic oxides and basic hydroxides.

A basic oxide is a metallic oxide which contains ions, O^{2-}, and reacts with acid to form a salt and water only, e.g. calcium oxide, CaO.

A basic hydroxide is a metallic hydroxide which contains hydroxyl ions, OH^-, and reacts with acid to form a salt and water only, e.g. iron(III) hydroxide, $Fe(OH)_3$.

The nature of metallic hydroxides depends upon the position of the metal in the reactivity series (see p. 36).

An alkali is a basic hydroxide which is soluble in water.

Examples: sodium hydroxide (caustic soda) NaOH
potassium hydroxide (caustic potash) KOH
calcium hydroxide (slaked lime) $Ca(OH)_2$

Alkalis possess all the properties of basic hydroxides in general but also have the very important property of being soluble in water; this enables them to take part in many reactions in solution which the insoluble basic hydroxides are unable to.

44

Neutralization is the reaction between an acid and an alkali in solution to form a salt and water.

Examples of neutralization

Base or alkali	Acid	Salt	Water
$K^+ + OH^-$	$+ H^+ + Cl^- \rightarrow$	$K^+ + Cl^-$	$+ H_2O$
$2Na^+ + 2OH^-$	$+ 2H^+ + SO_4^{2-} \rightarrow$	$2Na^+ + SO_4^{2-}$	$+ 2H_2O$

A strong base and a strong acid are fully dissociated into ions in dilute solution. The salt formed on neutralization is also fully dissociated into ions. Therefore when a strong acid is neutralized by a strong base the only reaction occurring is the production of water molecules from hydroxide ions (from the base) and hydroxonium ions (hydrated H^+ ions from the acid), i.e.

$$OH^- + H_3O^+ \rightarrow 2H_2O$$

This means that the energy liberated when a molar solution of a strong acid, e.g. HCl, H_2SO_4, is neutralized by a molar solution of a strong base, e.g. NaOH, KOH, is a constant ($= 57.3$ kJ).

Salts

A salt is a substance formed when one or more hydrogen ions, H^+, in an acid are replaced by a metallic cation.

A normal salt is a substance formed when all the hydrogen ions, H^+, in an acid which are capable of being replaced have been replaced by metallic cations (see examples below).

An acid salt is a substance formed when only some of the hydrogen ions, H^+, capable of being replaced in an acid molecule have been replaced by metallic cations, i.e. the negative ion the salt formed is capable of further ionization to produce H^+.

Acid		Basicity	Negative ion	Normal salt	Acid salt
Hydro-chloric	HCl	1	Cl^-	NaCl	—
Sulphuric	H_2SO_4	2	$\begin{cases} HSO_4^- \\ SO_4^{2-} \end{cases}$	Na_2SO_4	$NaHSO_4$
Nitrous	HNO_2	1	NO_2^-	$NaNO_2$	—
Nitric	HNO_3	1	NO_3^-	$NaNO_3$	—
Carbonic	H_2CO_3	2	$\begin{cases} HCO_3^- \\ CO_3^{2-} \end{cases}$	Na_2CO_3	$NaHCO_3$
Formic	HCOOH	1	$HCOO^-$	HCOONa	—
Acetic	CH_3COOH	1	CH_3COO^-	CH_3COONa	—

A basic salt is one in which the O^{2-} or OH^- ion is retained, together with a metallic ion and a negative ion from an acid, e.g.

Basic hydroxide	Basic salt	Normal salt
$Zn(OH)_2$	$Zn(OH)Cl$	$ZnCl_2$
$Mg(OH)_2$	$Mg(OH)Cl$	$MgCl_2$
$Pb(OH)_2$	$3Pb^{2+}, 2OH^-, 2CO_3^{2-}$	$PbCO_3$
	white lead	

Solubilities of salts in water

Salt	Soluble	Insoluble
Chlorides	Most are soluble except:	lead chloride ($PbCl_2$) silver chloride ($AgCl$)
Sulphates	Most are soluble except:	lead sulphate ($PbSO_4$) barium sulphate ($BaSO_4$) calcium sulphate ($CaSO_4$) is sparingly soluble
Nitrates	All are soluble	
Carbonates	Only three are soluble: sodium carbonate (Na_2CO_3) potassium carbonate (K_2CO_3) ammonium carbonate (($NH_4)_2CO_3$)	All others are insoluble
Hydrogen-carbonates	All are soluble	

Note:

1. All sodium, potassium and ammonium salts are soluble in water.
2. Lead(II) chloride is fairly soluble in hot water but insoluble in cold.
3. Calcium sulphate is sparingly soluble in water but is considered to be insoluble for preparation purposes.

Preparation of salts

Preparation of an insoluble salt To make the insoluble salt XY, a solution containing the soluble salt XA (which contains the cation X^+) is mixed with a solution containing the soluble salt BY (which contains the anion Y^-). Then $XA + BY \rightarrow XY + AB$, XY being precipitated out. For example the preparation of lead sulphate

$$Pb(NO_3)_2(aq) + Na_2SO_4(aq) \rightarrow PbSO_4(s) + 2NaNO_3(aq)$$

Preparation of soluble salts of metals (except those of Na or K). The metal, metal oxide or metal carbonate, is added in small portions to the appropriate acid until the acid is neutralized. For example, the preparation of copper(II) chloride

$$CuCO_3(s) + 2HCl(aq) \rightarrow CuCl_2(aq) + CO_2(g) + H_2O(l)$$

Preparation of salts of sodium, potassium and ammonium Preparation is by the neutralization of the appropriate acid with the appropriate alkali.

$$Acid + alkali \rightarrow salt + water$$

For example preparation of potassium nitrate

$$KOH(aq) + HNO_3(aq) \rightarrow KNO_3(aq) + H_2O(l)$$

Preparation of an acid salt As for the preparation of a normal salt but using twice the volume of acid or half the volume of alkali as was required for the normal salt.

The pH scale The strengths of various acids and bases can be measured according to this scale. The pH of a solution is the negative logarithm to the base 10 of the hydrogen ion concentration measured in mol/dm^3. The pH $= -\log_{10}[H^+]$. The scale ranges from 1–14, strong acids have a low pH of 1 to 2 and strong alkalis a pH of 13 to 14. Neutral solutions have a pH of 7.

pH 1 2 3 4 5 6 7 8 9 10 11 12 13 14

increasing acidity ← | ↑ neutral | → increasing alkalinity

Universal indicator is a mixture of indicators which has a range of colours over the pH scale and can therefore be used to indicate pH not just acidity or alkalinity.

Indicators are chemical compounds, usually vegetable dyes, which by changing their colour will indicate whether a solution is acidic or alkaline.

Indicator	Colour in acids	Colour in alkalis
Red litmus	red	blue
Blue litmus	red	blue
Phenolphthalein	colourless or white	pink
Methyl orange	red	yellow
Screened methyl orange	red	green

Metals: Occurrence and Extraction

The table below lists the metals in order of reactivity and indicates the manner in which the elements are manufactured from their ores. Metals low down in the series are frequently formed as the free elements but are still often obtained from the ores because the amounts found of the free metal are not sufficient for industrial purposes.

K
Na
Ca
Mg
Al
1. Very reactive.
2. Occur chiefly as the chloride. (Calcium chiefly as the carbonate.) Never found as the free element.
3. Extracted by electrolysis of their molten salts.

Zn
Fe
Pb
1. Moderately reactive.
2. Occur as oxides, carbonates or sulphides.
3. Extracted by reduction with carbon or carbon monoxide.

Cu
Hg
Ag
Au
1. Not very reactive.
2. May be found in nature as the free element.

Occurrence of sodium Occurs mainly as the chloride (never as metallic sodium). Other sources include sodium carbonate and sodium nitrate (Chile saltpetre).

Extraction of sodium and potassium Both metals are extracted in a similar manner by electrolysis of their fused chlorides. Sodium is extracted by the Down's process. Fused (molten) sodium chloride is electrolyzed at 600 °C (strontium chloride is added in small amounts to lower the melting point of salt from 800 °C to 600 °C) in a Down's cell. The cell consists of an outer iron shell enclosing an iron gauze diaphragm which screens the carbon anode from the ring shaped iron cathode that surrounds it and so prevents mixing of the sodium and chlorine.

At cathode (iron)
$Na^+ + e \rightarrow Na$

At anode (carbon)
$2Cl^- - e \rightarrow Cl_2$

Chlorine is a valuable product of the process.

Occurrence of calcium Occurs abundantly as calcium carbonate, $CaCO_3$, in the form of chalk, limestone, marble and Iceland spar. It also occurs as dolomite, $CaCO_3.MgCO_3$, gypsum, $CaSO_4.2H_2O$ and as anhydrite, $CaSO_4$. It occurs less abundantly as fluorspar, CaF_2, and as calcium phosphate, $Ca_3(PO_4)_2$.

Extraction of calcium, Ca By the electrolysis of fused (molten) calcium chloride in a graphite (carbon) container which is the anode, the cathode being an iron rod dipped just below the surface of the calcium chloride. Calcium fluoride is added to lower the melting point. Calcium forms at the cathode, chlorine is evolved at the anode.

At cathode (iron)   *At anode* (graphite)
$$Ca^{2+} + 2e \rightarrow Ca \qquad\qquad 2Cl^- - 2e \rightarrow Cl_2$$

Occurrence of magnesium A rich source of supply is magnesium chloride in sea water. Also occurs as magnesium carbonate (magnesite), $MgCO_3$, magnesium sulphate (Epsom salts), $MgSO_4.7H_2O$, and as dolomite, $CaCO_3.MgCO_3$.

Extraction of magnesium, Mg By the electrolysis of fused (molten) magnesium chloride in an iron container which is the cathode. The anode is a carbon rod dipping into the magnesium chloride. Magnesium is formed at the cathode and rises, in its molten state, to the surface of the cell which is covered with an inert gas to prevent oxidation. Chlorine is evolved at the anode. The magnesium is protected from the anodic chlorine by a porcelain sheath surrounding the anode.

At cathode (iron)   *At anode* (carbon)
$$Mg^{2+} + 2e \rightarrow Mg \qquad\qquad 2Cl^- - 2e \rightarrow Cl_2$$

Occurrence of aluminium Occurs widely as the metal. Compounds of it are quite abundant, aluminium occurring as a silicate in most clays and rocks, e.g. mica $K_2Al_2Si_6O_{16}$, kaolin (china clay) $Al_2Si_2O_7.2H_2O$. Other ores include bauxite $Al_2O_3.2H_2O$, corundum Al_2O_3 and cryolite Na_3AlF_6.

Extraction of aluminium, Al By the electrolysis of purified bauxite (alumina, Al_2O_3). The alumina is mixed with a small amount of cryolite (Na_3AlF_6) and calcium fluoride to lower the melting point and increase fluidity of the cell feed. The cathode is the carbon lining of the container, the anodes are carbon rods dipped into the alumina. Molten aluminium, formed at the cathode, collects at the bottom of the cell and is siphoned off. Oxygen is liberated at the anodes, which are gradually oxidized by the oxygen necessitating their regular replacement.

Occurrence of zinc Occurs mainly as zinc carbonate (calamine), $ZnCO_3$ and zinc sulphide (zinc blende), ZnS.

Extraction of zinc, Zn By the reduction of zinc oxide by heating with coke. Zinc oxide is first obtained by roasting the ores, zinc carbonate and zinc sulphide, in air, e.g.

$$2ZnS(s) + 3O_2(g) \rightarrow 2ZnO(s) + 2SO_2(g)$$

The sulphur dioxide is often used for the manufacture of sulphuric acid.

The zinc oxide is reduced to zinc by heating it with coke in a fireclay retort. The zinc distils out of the retort and condenses to molten zinc in a condenser attached to the end of the retort.

$$ZnO(s) + C(s) \rightarrow Zn(s) + CO(g)$$

Occurrence of iron It occurs widely as the metal. The chief ores are haematite, Fe_2O_3, magnetite, Fe_3O_4 and spathic iron ore $FeCO_3$.

Extraction of iron, Fe By reduction of iron(III) oxide by coke. Iron(III) oxide is heated with limestone and coke in a blast furnace. The reactions occurring are as follows:

1. The coke burns to form carbon monoxide and carbon dioxide, which is reduced with more coke to carbon monoxide

$$2C(s) + O_2(g) \rightarrow 2CO(g)$$
$$C(s) + O_2(g) \rightarrow CO_2(g)$$
$$CO_2(g) + C(s) \rightarrow 2CO(g)$$

2. The carbon monoxide reduces iron(III) oxide to iron, which collects at the bottom of the furnace, from where it is tapped off.

$$Fe_2O_3(s) + 3CO(g) \rightarrow 2Fe(s) + 3CO_2(g)$$

3. The limestone decomposes

$$CaCO_3(s) \rightleftharpoons CaO(s) + CO_2(g)$$

The carbon dioxide reacts with the coke to form carbon monoxide.

4. The quicklime produced, CaO, reacts with the siliceous material in the ore to form a slag which floats on the top of the molten iron from where it can be tapped.

$$CaO(s) + SiO_2(s) \rightarrow CaSiO_3(s)$$

Pig iron (cast iron) is impure iron containing 3–5 per cent of carbon with traces of silicon, phosphorous, sulphur and manganese. It is brittle, cannot be welded and is of low tensile strength.

Wrought iron is the purest form of iron and is obtained from cast iron by heating it with iron(II) oxide. It has a higher m.p. than cast iron, is malleable and can be welded when hot.

Steel is a material containing iron and a small proportion of carbon. It is hard, tough and can be made of high tensile strength. It is used extensively in a wide range of applications.

Occurrence of lead Lead occurs widely as the metal. The main ore is galena (lead sulphide) PbS.

Extraction of lead, Pb By the reduction of lead(II) oxide by heating with coke. The lead sulphide ore is first roasted to obtain the oxide. The oxide is then reduced to lead by heating it with coke in a small blast furnace.

$$PbO(s) + C(s) \rightarrow Pb(s) + CO(g)$$

Occurrence of copper Occurs as the free metal. Principal ores are copper pyrites, $CuFeS_2$, cuprite Cu_2O, copper(I) sulphide (Cu_2S) and malachite, $CuCO_3.Cu(OH)_2$.

Extraction of copper, Cu By reduction of copper(I) sulphide by roasting in air. Copper(I) oxide is first obtained by roasting the ore copper pyrites in air.

$$2CuFeS_2(s) + 4O_2(g) \rightarrow Cu_2S(s) + 3SO_2(g) + 2FeO(s)$$

The products are then heated with sand to convert iron(II) oxide into slag which is removed. The fused copper(I) sulphide is then reduced to copper by heating it in a converter through which a regulated supply of air is blown.

$$Cu_2S(s) + O_2(g) \rightarrow 2Cu(s) + SO_2(g)$$

The copper is further purified by electrolysis.

Metals and Their Compounds

Traditionally, metals have been distinguished from non-metals by differences in their physical properties, e.g. thermal and electrical conductivity, ductility, etc. This approach has been largely superseded and nowadays the differences between metals and non-metals is being studied in terms of their chemical behaviour.

Metal	Series of Compounds formed
Sodium	Na(I)
Calcium	Ca(II)
Magnesium	Mg(II)
Aluminium	Al(III)
Zinc	Zn(II)
Iron	Fe(II) and Fe(III)
Lead	Pb(II) and Pb(IV)
Copper	Cu(I) and Cu(II)

A metal is defined as an element which forms ions by losing electrons. The **valency** of a metal is equal to the number of electrons lost per atom. The charge on the metal ion is positive and equal in magnitude to the valency.

$$K - e \rightarrow K^+ \quad \text{potassium is univalent}$$
$$Ca - 2e \rightarrow Ca^{2+} \quad \text{calcium is divalent}$$
$$Al - 3e \rightarrow Al^{3+} \quad \text{aluminium is trivalent}$$

Comparison of the chemical properties of metals and non-metals

Metals

1. Oxides of metals are basic and, if soluble in water, form alkalis.
2. Metals replace hydrogen in acids forming salts.
3. Metallic chlorides are electrovalent salts containing Cl^- and are electrolytes.
4. Metals form few stable hydrides. The hydrides of Na, K and Ca are salt-like and contain the H^- ion.
5. Metals are reducing agents.

Non-metals

1. Characteristic oxides of non-metals are acidic; other oxides are acidic or neutral.
2. Non-metals are unable to form salts in this way.
3. Non-metallic chlorides are covalent, non-electrolytes.
4. Non-metals form many stable hydrides; they are covalent non-electrolytes, e.g. CH_4, PH_3.
5. They are oxidizing agents.

Comparison of the physical properties of metals and non-metals

Metals	Non-metals
1. Usually high melting and boiling points.	1. Usually low melting and boiling points.
2. Good conductors of heat and electricity.	2. Generally bad conductors of heat and electricity.
3. Malleable and ductile (can be drawn into a wire).	3. Generally brittle, not malleable or ductile.
4. Sonorous.	4. Not sonorous.
5. Lustrous.	5. Not usually lustrous.
6. Usually high density.	6. Low density.
7. Usually high tensile strength.	7. Low tensile strength.

Sodium and its compounds

Properties of sodium, Na

It is a soft shiny metal, easily cut with a knife.

Action on exposure to air	Initially forms sodium oxide which then combines with moisture in the air to form sodium hydroxide. After a time the carbon dioxide in the air combines with the hydroxide to form the carbonate $4Na(s) + O_2(g) \rightarrow 2Na_2O(s)$ – sodium oxide $Na_2O(s) + H_2O(l) \rightarrow 2NaOH(aq)$ $2NaOH(s) + CO_2(g) \rightarrow Na_2CO_3(s) + H_2O(l)$
Combustion	Burns with a characteristic golden-yellow flame to form sodium peroxide $2Na(s) + O_2(g) \rightarrow Na_2O_2(s)$ – sodium peroxide
Action on cold water	Reacts violently with the formation of sodium hydroxide and the liberation of hydrogen $2Na(s) + 2H_2O(l) \rightarrow 2NaOH(aq) + H_2(g)$
Action on dilute acids	Displaces hydrogen with explosive violence $2Na(s) + H_2SO_4(aq) \rightarrow Na_2SO_4(aq) + H_2(g)$ $2Na(s) + 2H^+(aq) \rightarrow 2Na^+(aq) + H_2(g)$

Uses of sodium

1. In the manufacture of sodium cyanide, NaCN, which is used in the extraction of gold.
2. In the manufacture of sodamide, $NaNH_2$.
3. In manufacturing sodium peroxide, Na_2O_2.
4. In sodium vapour lamps for street lighting, etc.

Properties of sodium hydroxide (caustic soda), NaOH

It is a white deliquescent solid.

Action on exposure to air	Deliquesces (see p. 70), forming a solution which then absorbs carbon dioxide from the air to form a crystalline solid, washing soda or sodium carbonate decahydrate. $2NaOH(s) + CO_2(g) + 9H_2O(l) \rightarrow Na_2CO_3.10H_2O(s)$ On standing, efflorescence occurs, the monohydrate being formed.
With litmus	It is an alkali which turns red litmus blue.
Precipitation of insoluble hydroxides	Being soluble sodium hydroxide is used to precipitate insoluble hydroxides from solutions of soluble salts, e.g. $FeCl_3(aq) + 3NaOH(aq) \rightarrow 3NaCl(aq) + Fe(OH)_3(s)$ $Fe^{3+}(aq) + 3OH^-(aq) \rightarrow Fe(OH)_3(s)$
Heating with ammonium salts	Ammonia is liberated. $NH_4Cl(aq) + NaOH(aq) \rightarrow$ $\qquad\qquad\qquad NaCl(aq) + H_2O(l) + NH_3(g)$ $NH_4^+(aq) + OH^-(aq) \rightarrow NH_3(g) + H_2O(l)$

Uses of sodium hydroxide

1. In rayon manufacture and (2) in soap manufacture.
3. In purifying crude bauxite before extraction of aluminium.

Properties of sodium carbonate, Na_2CO_3

It is a white deliquescent solid, which in the form of $Na_2CO_3.10H_2O$ is known as washing soda.

Action on exposure to air	Effloresces (see p. 70) to form the monohydrate. $Na_2CO_3.10H_2O(s) \rightarrow Na_2CO_3.H_2O(s) + 9H_2O(g)$
Action on heating	The hydrated form $(Na_2CO_3.10H_2O)$ loses its water of crystallization to yield anhydrous sodium carbonate, which is stable to heat. $Na_2CO_3.10H_2O(s) \rightarrow Na_2CO_3(s) + 10H_2O(g)$
Action with acids	A salt and water are formed with the liberation of hydrogen, e.g. $Na_2CO_3(aq) + 2HCl(aq) \rightarrow$ $\qquad\qquad\qquad 2NaCl(aq) + H_2O(l) + CO_2(g)$
As a carbonate precipitator	If a solution of sodium carbonate is added to a solution of a metal salt, other than those of potassium or ammonium, the corresponding carbonate is precipitated, e.g. $Cu(NO_3)_2(aq) + Na_2CO_3(aq) \rightarrow$ $\qquad\qquad\qquad CuCO_3(s) + 2NaNO_3(aq)$

Uses of sodium carbonate
1. In the manufacture of sodium hydroxide (Gossage's process).
2. In the manufacture of glass, soap powders and paper.
3. As a domestic water-softener.

Properties of sodium hydrogencarbonate (baking soda), $NaHCO_3$

Action of heat	Decomposes to form the carbonate $2NaHCO_3(s) \rightarrow Na_2CO_3(s) + H_2O(g) + CO_2(g)$ This distinguishes it from sodium carbonate which is unaffected by heat.
Action with dilute acids	Effervesces with the liberation of carbon dioxide, e.g. $2NaHCO_3(s) + 2HCl(aq) \rightarrow$ $2NaCl(aq) + 2H_2O(l) + 2CO_2(g)$

Uses of sodium hydrogencarbonate
1. In health salts and stomach powders.
2. In baking powder as a raising agent. On heating, carbon dioxide and steam are liberated forming bubbles which raise the material.
3. In dry fire extinguishers.

Properties of sodium nitrate (Chile saltpetre), $NaNO_3$
It is a white crystalline solid, very soluble in water.

Action of heat	It melts and eventually decomposes to give sodium nitrite and oxygen. $2NaNO_3(s) \rightarrow 2NaNO_2(s) + O_2(g)$
Heating with concentrated sulphuric acid	Nitric acid is produced (an example of a more volatile acid being displaced from its salt by a less volatile acid) $NaNO_3(s) + H_2SO_4(aq) \xrightarrow{conc.} NaHSO_4(aq) + HNO_3(aq)$

Uses of sodium nitrate
1. In fertilizers, this being its most important application.
2. In the manufacture of nitric acid.
3. In fireworks and flares.
4. In gunpowder.

Properties of sodium chloride (common salt), NaCl
Sodium chloride is a white crystalline solid, soluble in water.

Heating	Stable to heat
Heating with concentrated sulphuric acid	Hydrogen chloride gas is evolved, which dissolves in water to form hydrochloric acid. $NaCl(s) + H_2SO_4(aq) \rightarrow NaHSO_4(aq) + HCl(g)$

Uses of sodium chloride
1. In cooking, to enhance the taste of the food and as a preservative.
2. In the manufacture of bleaching agents.
3. In the production of caustic soda, baking soda and Na_2SO_4.
4. In soap making, to 'salt out' soap.

Potassium and its compounds

1. Potassium possesses similar chemical properties to sodium but is slightly more reactive.
2. The compounds of potassium behave in a similar way chemically to those of sodium.
3. Potassium compounds are generally less soluble in water than those of sodium (main exceptions are KOH, K_2CO_3, $KHCO_3$).

Calcium and its compounds

Properties of calcium, Ca
Calcium is a fairly soft, grey metal.

Exposure to air	Quickly tarnishes owing to the formation of a crust of calcium oxide.
Combustion	Burns with a brick-red flame to calcium oxide $2Ca(s) + O_2(g) \rightarrow 2CaO(s)$
Action with cold water	Reacts readily with the liberation of hydrogen $Ca(s) + 2H_2O(l) \rightarrow Ca(OH)_2(aq) + H_2(g)$
Action with dilute acid	Displaces hydrogen, e.g. $Ca(s) + H_2SO_4(aq) \rightarrow CaSO_4(s) + H_2(g)$

Uses of calcium
1. As a deoxidizer in the steel industry.
2. As a reducing agent in the extraction of the metal thorium.

Properties of calcium oxide (quicklime), CaO
It is a fine white powder.

Action with water	Reacts vigorously to form calcium hydroxide $CaO(s) + H_2O(l) \rightarrow Ca(OH)_2(aq)$
Action with dilute acids (HCl or HNO$_3$)	With dilute hydrochloric and nitric acids the corresponding salt is formed, e.g. $CaO(s) + 2HCl(aq) \rightarrow CaCl_2(aq) + H_2O(l)$ The reaction with sulphuric acid is short-lived owing to the forming of a thick layer of insoluble calcium sulphate round the oxide.

Uses of calcium oxide
1. After slaking it is used in the building trade to make mortar.
2. It is hygroscopic and is used to dry ammonia gas.

Limewater is a solution of calcium hydroxide. It is used to test for carbon dioxide gas. If carbon dioxide is bubbled through limewater for a short time it turns milky, but with excess carbon dioxide a clear solution is again obtained.

Slaking of lime is the addition of water to calcium oxide (quicklime) to produce calcium hydroxide (slaked lime).

$$CaO(s) + H_2O(l) \rightarrow Ca(OH)_2(aq)$$

Properties of calcium hydroxide, $Ca(OH)_2$
It is slightly soluble in water. In solution it is known as limewater.

Action with acids	Being a basic hydroxide it forms salts, e.g. $Ca(OH)_2(s) + 2HCl(aq) \rightarrow CaCl_2(aq) + 2H_2O(l)$
Action with ammonium salts	It liberates ammonia $2NH_4NO_3(aq) + Ca(OH)_2(aq) \rightarrow Ca(NO_3)_2(aq) + 2NH_3(g) + 2H_2O(l)$
Action with chlorine	With solid $Ca(OH)_2$ bleaching powder is formed $Ca(OH)_2(s) + Cl_2(g) \rightarrow CaOCl_2(s) + H_2O(l)$ With a conc. solution of $Ca(OH)_2$, calcium chloride, and calcium hypochlorite are formed $2Ca(OH)_2(aq) + 2Cl_2(g) \rightarrow Ca(OCl)_2(s) + CaCl_2(aq) + 2H_2O(l)$

Uses of calcium hydroxide
1. In the manufacture of mortar.
2. In agriculture, to reduce the acidity of the soil.

Properties of calcium carbonate, $CaCO_3$

Action with acids (except sulphuric acid)	Reacts to form a salt, carbon dioxide, water $CaCO_3(s) + 2HCl(aq) \rightarrow CaCl_2(aq) + H_2O(l) + CO_2(g)$
Action on strong heating	Decomposes reversibly $CaCO_3(s) \rightleftharpoons CaO(s) + CO_2(g)$

Uses of calcium carbonate
1. In the manufacture of cement.
2. In making quicklime in a lime kiln.

Properties of calcium hydrogencarbonate, $Ca(HCO_3)_2$
Calcium hydrogencarbonate is responsible for the temporary hardness of water and exists only in solution. On heating it breaks down to form calcium carbonate, carbon dioxide and water.

Calcium sulphate, $CaSO_4$, occurs naturally as anhydrite and gypsum. It is insoluble in water. Gypsum is mainly used for the manufacture of plaster of paris.

Plaster of paris is calcium sulphate hemihydrate, $(CaSO_4)_2.H_2O$. It is made by heating gypsum to 120–130 °C. When mixed with water, plaster of paris sets to a hard mass of interweaving needles of gypsum, at the same time expanding slightly. It is used in statuary for making casts and in surgery for immobilization of fractures, and in wall-plasters and cements.

Calcium chloride, $CaCl_2$, is very deliquescent and is hence used as a drying agent for gases, except for ammonia with which it forms a compound.

Calcium nitrate, $Ca(NO_3)_2$, is manufactured by the action of dilute nitric acid on limestone. When heated it decomposes to give calcium oxide, nitrogen dioxide and oxygen. It is used mainly as a fertilizer when it is sometimes known as nitrate of chalk.

Magnesium and compounds

Properties of magnesium, Mg

Magnesium is a soft silvery-grey metal, stable in dry air but tarnishing rapidly in moist air to form the oxide.

Action with water	Reacts slowly in hot water but burns in steam $Mg(s) + 2H_2O(g) \rightarrow Mg(OH)_2(s) + H_2(g)$
Combustion	Burns with a brilliant white light to form the oxide and a small amount of the nitride $2Mg(s) + O_2(g) \rightarrow 2MgO(s)$ $3Mg(s) + N_2(g) \rightarrow Mg_3N_2(s)$
Action with dilute acids	Reacts vigorously to form a salt and hydrogen $Mg(s) + 2HCl(aq) \rightarrow MgCl_2(aq) + H_2(g)$
Heating with carbon dioxide, sulphur dioxide and nitrous oxide	Burns to form the oxide, releasing the non-metal $2Mg(s) + CO_2(g) \rightarrow 2MgO(s) + C(s)$ $2Mg(s) + SO_2(g) \rightarrow 2MgO(s) + S(s)$ $Mg(s) + N_2O(g) \rightarrow MgO(s) + N_2(g)$
As a reducing agent	Reduces most metallic oxides on heating $3Mg(s) + Al_2O_3(s) \rightarrow 2Al(s) + 3MgO(s)$
Heating with non-metals	Combines directly, e.g. $Mg(s) + Cl_2(g) \rightarrow MgCl_2(s)$

Preparation of magnesium oxide, MgO

1. Burning magnesium in oxygen
$$2Mg(s) + O_2(g) \rightarrow 2MgO(s)$$

2. Heating magnesium carbonate, hydroxide or nitrate, e.g.
$$Mg(OH)_2(s) \rightarrow MgO(s) + H_2O(g)$$

Properties of magnesium oxide, MgO

It is a fine white powder.

Solubility in water	Slightly soluble, forming an alkaline solution $MgO(s) + H_2O(l) \rightarrow Mg(OH)_2(aq)$
Action with dilute acids	As a basic oxide it reacts to form salts $MgO(s) + 2HCl(aq) \rightarrow MgCl_2(aq) + H_2O(l)$

Uses of magnesium oxide

1. As a refractory lining for furnaces etc.
2. In medicines, to cure acidity of the stomach.

Aluminium and its compounds

Properties of aluminium, Al

Aluminium is a silvery-white metal of low density. It is a reactive metal which quickly forms a protective layer of oxide.

With hydrochloric acid	With dilute acid it reacts slowly; with conc. acid it reacts rapidly, liberating hydrogen. $2Al(s) + 6HCl(aq) \rightarrow 2AlCl_3(aq) + 3H_2(g)$
With sulphuric acid	Only reacts with the concentrated acid $2Al(s) + 6H_2SO_4(aq) \rightarrow Al_2(SO_4)_3(aq) + 6H_2O(l) + 3SO_2(g)$
With nitric acid	No reaction
With sodium hydroxide solution	Reacts violently giving the aluminate and hydrogen $2Al(s) + 2NaOH(aq) + 2H_2O(l) \rightarrow 2NaAlO_2(aq) + 3H_2(g)$
With non-metals	Reacts on heating, e.g. $2Al(s) + 3Cl_2(g) \rightarrow 2AlCl_3(g)$

Uses of aluminium

1. In alloys, e.g. Duralumin (Al, Mg, Cu, Mn).
2. In cooking utensils and paint.
3. In the thermit process (see p. 60).

Thermit process If a mixture of iron(III) oxide and aluminium powder, known as thermit, is fired by burning a piece of magnesium ribbon inserted into it, a violent reaction occurs. Molten iron is produced with a slag of aluminium oxide floating on top.

$$Fe_2O_3(s) + 2Al(s) \rightarrow 2Fe(l) + Al_2O_3(s)$$

This reaction was formerly used in welding steel parts in situ.

Aluminium oxide, Al_2O_3 is a white insoluble powder *prepared by* the action of heat on aluminium hydroxide. It is an amphoteric oxide (see p. 68).

Basic $Al_2O_3(s) + 6HCl(aq) \rightarrow 2AlCl_3(aq) + 3H_2O(l)$
Acidic $Al_2O_3(s) + 2NaOH(aq) \rightarrow 2NaAlO_2(aq) + H_2O(l)$

The most important form of the oxide is as bauxite $Al_2O_3.2H_2O$ from which the metal is extracted.

Zinc and its compounds

Properties of zinc, Zn
Zinc is a hard, grey-white metal.

Exposure to air	Forms a protective coating of zinc oxide. Burns with a bluish-green flame to give the oxide $2Zn(s) + O_2(g) \rightarrow 2ZnO(s)$
With dilute HCl, H_2SO_4 and conc. HCl	Hydrogen is evolved, e.g. $Zn(s) + H_2SO_4(aq) \rightarrow ZnSO_4(aq) + H_2(g)$
With hot conc. sulphuric acid	Sulphur dioxide is evolved. $Zn(s) + 2H_2SO_4(aq) \rightarrow ZnSO_4(aq) + 2H_2O(l) + SO_2(g)$
With nitric acid	A variety of products is obtained depending upon the concentration and temperature
With hot aqueous sodium hydroxide	Reacts to give sodium zincate and hydrogen (zinc oxide is amphoteric) $Zn(s) + 2NaOH(aq) \rightarrow Na_2ZnO_2(aq) + H_2(g)$
With water	Zinc does not react with cold water but decomposes steam when heated in it $Zn(s) + H_2O(g) \rightarrow ZnO(s) + H_2(g)$

Uses of zinc
1. In the production of galvanized steel products.
2. In alloys, e.g. it alloys with copper to give the brasses.
3. In the manufacture of batteries and certain utensils.

Zinc oxide, ZnO

It is a white powder which on heating turns yellow.

Prepared by heating zinc nitrate, carbonate or hydroxide, e.g.

$$2Zn(NO_3)_2(s) \rightarrow 2ZnO(s) + 4NO_2(g) + O_2(g)$$

Zinc oxide is an amphoteric oxide forming zinc salts with acids, e.g.

$$ZnO(s) + 2HCl(aq) \rightarrow ZnCl_2(aq) + H_2O(aq)$$

and zincates with alkalis

$$ZnO(s) + 2NaOH(aq) \rightarrow Na_2ZnO_2(aq) + H_2O(l)$$

Zinc hydroxide, Zn(OH)$_2$

Prepared by adding sufficient sodium hydroxide solution to a solution of a zinc salt.

$$ZnSO_4(aq) + 2NaOH(aq) \rightarrow Zn(OH)_2(s) + Na_2SO_4(aq)$$

In excess alkali the precipitate dissolves to form the zincate.

$$Zn(OH)_2(s) + 2NaOH(aq) \rightarrow Na_2ZnO_2(aq) + 2H_2O(l)$$

Zinc carbonate, ZnCO$_3$

Prepared by the addition of sodium hydrogencarbonate solution to a solution of zinc sulphate

$$ZnSO_4(aq) + 2NaHCO_3(aq) \rightarrow$$
$$ZnCO_3(s) + Na_2SO_4(aq) + H_2O(l) + CO_2(g)$$

On heating, carbon dioxide is evolved and zinc oxide (yellow when hot, white when cold) remains.

$$ZnCO_3(s) \rightarrow ZnO(s) + CO_2(g)$$

Iron and its compounds

Properties of iron, Fe

Exposure to air	It is stable in dry air but rusts (see below) in moist air. Finely divided iron burns to form tri-iron tetroxide $3Fe(s) + 2O_2(g) \rightarrow Fe_3O_4(s)$
Action of steam	If heated strongly in steam forms tri-iron tetroxide and hydrogen (reversible reaction) $3Fe(s) + 4H_2O(g) \rightleftharpoons Fe_3O_4(s) + 4H_2(g)$
Action of dilute HCl and H$_2$SO$_4$ acids	Reacts with the liberation of hydrogen $Fe(s) + 2HCl(aq) \rightarrow FeCl_2(aq) + H_2(g)$
Action of nitric acid	With dilute acid a series of complex reactions occurs, with concentrated acid iron is yielded passive.
Action of non-metals	Readily combines with S or Cl on heating, e.g. $Fe(s) + S(s) \rightarrow FeS(s)$

Rusting of iron. In the presence of air and water (moist air), iron rusts to form hydrated iron(III) oxide ($Fe_2O_3.3H_2O$). In rusting, iron is merely reverting to its natural state.

Uses of iron

Iron has a multitude of uses. One of the major uses being its conversion into steel.

Comparison of the properties of iron(II) and iron(III) compounds

Iron(II) compounds	*Iron(III) compounds*
1. Reducing agents, because they can be oxidized to the iron(III) ion state $$Fe^{2+} - e \rightarrow Fe^{3+}$$	1. Oxidizing agents, because they can be reduced to the iron(II) ion state $$Fe^{3+} + e \rightarrow Fe^{2+}$$
2. Aqueous solutions are pale watery green	2. Aqueous solutions range in colour from dark yellow to reddish-brown
3. Solutions easily oxidized by the air to the iron(III) ion state	3. Solutions much more stable.
4. With alkaline solution forms a dirty-green precipitate of iron(II) hydroxide	4. With alkaline solution forms a brown gelatinous precipitate of iron(III) hydroxide

Iron(II) sulphate, FeSO$_4$

This is a watery-green coloured crystalline solid.
Prepared by dissolving iron wire in air-free dilute sulphuric acid.
$$Fe(s) + H_2SO_4(aq) \rightarrow FeSO_4(aq) + H_2(g)$$

The solution crystallizes out as $FeSO_4.7H_2O$.
On heating, iron(II) sulphate first loses its water of crystallization.
$$FeSO_4.7H_2O(s) \rightarrow FeSO_4(s) + 7H_2O(l)$$

and then decomposes liberating sulphur dioxide.
$$2FeSO_4(s) \rightarrow Fe_2O_3(s) + SO_2(g) + SO_3(g)$$

Iron(II) sulphate is used in the brown ring test for nitrates.

Iron(II) chloride, FeCl$_2$

Prepared by action of dilute hydrochloric acid on iron wire
$$Fe(s) + 2HCl(aq) \rightarrow FeCl_2(aq) + H_2(g)$$

Anhydrous iron(II) chloride, which is a white solid, is prepared by heating iron wire strongly in a stream of dry hydrogen chloride.
$$Fe(s) + 2HCl(aq) \rightarrow FeCl_2(s) + H_2(g)$$

Iron(II) hydroxide, Fe(OH)$_2$
Prepared by addition of sodium hydroxide solution to an iron(II) salt solution. It is a basic oxide, reacting with acids to form salts

$$Fe(OH)_2(aq) + 2HCl(aq) \rightarrow FeCl_2(aq) + 2H_2O(l)$$

Iron(II) sulphide, FeS
A black insoluble compound, *prepared by* heating iron filings with sulphur. It is used in the production of hydrogen sulphide by reaction with dilute acids.

$$Fe(s) + S(s) \rightarrow FeS(s)$$

Iron(III) oxide, Fe$_2$O$_3$
This is a dark red compound which is found naturally.
Prepared in the laboratory by
(i) heating iron(II) sulphate strongly

$$2FeSO_4(s) \rightarrow Fe_2O_3(s) + SO_2(g) + SO_3(g)$$

(ii) heating iron(III) hydroxide strongly.

$$2Fe(OH)_3(s) \rightarrow Fe_2O_3(s) + 3H_2O(g)$$

It is amphoteric reacting with acids to form salts

$$Fe_2O_3(s) + 6HCl(aq) \rightarrow 2FeCl_3(aq) + 3H_2O(l)$$

and with bases to form ferrites.

$$2NaOH(aq) + Fe_2O_3 \rightarrow 2NaFeO_2(aq) + H_2O(l)$$

It can be reduced by heating with hydrogen, carbon, or carbon monoxide.

Tri-iron tetroxide (ferrosoferric oxide), Fe$_3$O$_4$
It is a black compound which occurs naturally as magnetite and is a natural magnet. *Prepared by* heating iron in steam.

$$3Fe(s) + 4H_2O(g) \rightleftharpoons Fe_3O_4(s) + 4H_2(g)$$

In its reactions it may be regarded as a mixture of FeO and Fe$_2$O$_3$,
e.g. $Fe_3O_4(s) + 8HCl(aq) \rightarrow FeCl_2(aq) + 2FeCl_3(aq) + 4H_2O(l)$

Iron(III) hydroxide, Fe(OH)$_3$ is a reddish-brown compound
prepared by adding sodium hydroxide solution to a solution of an iron(III) salt.

Iron(III) sulphate, Fe$_2$(SO$_4$)$_3$ is a yellowish compound
prepared by oxidizing iron(II) sulphate by nitric acid in the presence of sulphuric acid.

$$6Fe^{2+}(aq) + 6H^+(aq) + 2HNO_3(aq) \rightarrow$$
$$6Fe^{3+}(aq) + 4H_2O(l) + 2NO(g)$$

It forms alums, for example K$_2$SO$_4$.Fe$_2$(SO$_4$)$_3$.24H$_2$O which can be readily purified by crystallization.

Tests for iron(II) and iron(III) compounds

Test	Iron(II)	Iron(III)
1. Colour	Generally green	Dark yellow to brown
2. Addition of alkali (NaOH or KOH)	Green precipitate of iron(II) hydroxide which turns brown on exposure to air	Reddish-brown precipitate of iron(III) hydroxide

Lead and its compounds

Properties of lead, Pb
Lead is a soft, heavy grey metal

Action of air and water	Tarnishes slowly forming a coating of lead hydroxide and lead carbonate.
Combustion	Tarnishes slowly to form lead oxide.
Action of conc. sulphuric acid	Lead is not attacked by dilute hydrochloric acid or dilute sulphuric acid but by concentrated sulphuric acid. $Pb(s) + 2H_2SO_4(aq) \rightarrow PbSO_4(s) + 2H_2O(l) + SO_2(g)$
Action of dilute nitric acid	Reacts to form the nitrate and nitric oxide $3Pb(s) + 8HNO_3(aq) \rightarrow$ $3Pb(NO_3)_2(aq) + 4H_2O(l) + 2NO(g)$
Action of chlorine	Forms lead(II) chloride $Pb(s) + Cl_2(g) \rightarrow PbCl_2(s)$

Uses of lead
1. In radiation shields and accumulators.
2. In the manufacture of alloys including solder and pewter.

Lead(II) oxide (litharge), PbO
This is a yellow solid, easily reduced to the metal by heating with carbon, hydrogen or carbon monoxide.
Prepared by heating any lead salt except the chloride, e.g.
$$2Pb(NO_3)_2(s) \rightarrow 2PbO(s) + 4NO_2(g) + O_2(g)$$

It is an amphoteric oxide reacting with acids to form salts and with caustic alkalis to form plumbites, e.g.
$$PbO(s) + 2HNO_3(aq) \rightarrow Pb(NO_3)_2(aq) + H_2O(l)$$
$$PbO(s) + 2NaOH(aq) \rightarrow Na_2PbO_2(aq) + H_2O(l)$$

Lead(II) hydroxide, Pb(OH)$_2$ is *prepared by* the action of an alkali on a solution of a lead salt. A white precipitate of the hydroxide is formed which dissolves in excess alkali.

Lead(II) nitrate, $Pb(NO_3)_2$ This is a white crystalline solid which is the only soluble lead salt. *Prepared by* the action of dilute nitric acid on lead, the oxide or carbonate, e.g.

$$PbCO_3(s) + 2HNO_3(aq) \rightarrow Pb(NO_3)_2(aq) + H_2O(l) + CO_2(g)$$

On heating the lead(II) nitrate decomposes according to

$$2Pb(NO_3)_2(s) \rightarrow 2PbO(s) + 4NO_2(g) + O_2(g)$$

Lead(II) chloride, $PbCl_2$ is a heavy white powder *prepared by*
1. direct action of chlorine on lead $Pb(s) + Cl_2(g) \rightarrow PbCl_2(s)$

2. double decomposition of a soluble lead salt and a soluble chloride.

$$Pb(NO_3)_2(aq) + 2HCl(aq) \rightarrow PbCl_2(s) + 2HNO_3(aq)$$

It is soluble in hot water, insoluble in cold water.

Lead(IV) oxide, PbO_2, is a dark brown compound, *prepared by* heating nitric acid with red lead oxide.

$$Pb_3O_4(s) + 4HNO_3(aq) \rightarrow PbO_2(s) + 2Pb(NO_3)_2(s) + 2H_2O(l)$$

Read lead oxide, Pb_3O_4, is a bright red powder which behaves as if it were a mixture of lead(II) oxide, PbO, and lead(IV) oxide PbO_2. For example, with nitric acid

$$Pb_3O_4(s) + 4HNO_3(aq) \rightarrow 2Pb(NO_3)_2(s) + 2H_2O(l) + PbO_2(s)$$

Copper and its compounds

Properties of copper, Cu
It is a reddish-brown metal which is a good conductor of heat and electricity. In damp air it forms a layer of basic carbonate (verdigris), $CuCO_3.Cu(OH)_2$. Being lower than hydrogen in the activity series it does not react with water or liberate hydrogen from dilute acids.

Action of conc. sulphuric acid	Copper sulphate and sulphur dioxide are formed $Cu(s) + 2H_2SO_4(aq) \rightarrow CuSO_4(aq) + 2H_2O(l) + SO_2(g)$
Action of nitric acid	Reacts to give copper(I) nitrate and nitrogen oxides, e.g. $3Cu(s) + 8HNO_3(aq) \rightarrow$ $\qquad 3Cu(NO_3)_2(aq) + 4H_2O(l) + 2NO(g)$

Uses of copper
1. For conducting electric current.
2. For ornamental work, being little attacked by the air.
3. In alloys, e.g. brass (Cu and Zn), bronze (Cu and Sn).

Copper(I) oxide, Cu_2O, is a brick-red powder, insoluble in water but will react with acids to form copper(I) salts.

Copper(II) oxide, CuO

It is a black, insoluble powder.
Prepared by heating copper nitrate, carbonate or hydroxide, e.g.
$$CuCO_3(s) \rightarrow CuO(s) + CO_2(g)$$

It is a base which dissolves in acids to form salts
$$CuO(s) + 2HCl(aq) \rightarrow CuCl_2(aq) + H_2O(l)$$

It is readily reduced to copper by heating in hydrogen or carbon
$$CuO(s) + H_2(g) \rightarrow Cu(s) + H_2O(l)$$

Copper(II) hydroxide, Cu(OH)$_2$

Prepared by adding sodium hydroxide solution to a copper(II) sulphate solution; blue precipitate of the hydroxide is formed.
$$CuSO_4(aq) + 2NaOH(aq) \rightarrow Cu(OH)_2(aq) + Na_2SO_4(aq)$$

It is a base and reacts with acids to form salts
$$Cu(OH)_2(aq) + H_2SO_4(aq) \rightarrow CuSO_4(aq) + 2H_2O(l)$$

Copper(II) sulphate, CuSO$_4$.5H$_2$O

This is a blue crystalline solid which can be *prepared by* dissolving copper(II) oxide in dilute sulphuric acid. When heated the water of crystallization is lost, rendering the salt anhydrous.

Anhydrous copper(II) sulphate is a white powder. Water or liquids containing water will restore the blue colour if added to anhydrous copper sulphate. This is a common test for detecting the presence of water.
$$\underset{\text{blue}}{CuSO_4 5H_2O(s)} \rightarrow \underset{\text{white}}{CuSO_4(s)} + 5H_2O(l)$$

Copper(II) nitrate, Cu(NO$_3$)$_2$ is a royal blue crystalline solid which is deliquescent. *Prepared by* dissolving copper(II) oxide in dilute nitric acid.
$$CuO(s) + 2HNO_3(aq) \rightarrow Cu(NO_3)_2(aq) + H_2O(l)$$

It is very soluble in water and forms crystals of $Cu(NO_3)_2.3H_2O$ which decompose on heating.
$$2Cu(NO_3)_2(s) \rightarrow 2CuO(s) + 4NO_2(g) + O_2(g)$$

Copper(II) carbonate, CuCO$_3$

This is a green insoluble powder which is not known in a pure state. It breaks down very rapidly on heating.
$$CuCO_3(s) \rightarrow CuO(s) + CO_2(g)$$

Oxygen, Hydrogen and Water

Oxygen and its compounds

Laboratory preparation of oxygen (Method 3 is preferred)

1. Heating mercury(II) oxide or lead(IV) oxide or red lead oxide	$2HgO(s) \rightarrow 2Hg(l) + O_2(g)$ $2PbO_2(s) \rightarrow 2PbO(s) + O_2(g)$ $2Pb_3O_4(s) \rightarrow 6PbO(s) + O_2(g)$
2. Heating potassium chlorate with MnO_2 as catalyst	$2KClO_3(s) \rightarrow 2KCl(s) + 3O_2(g)$
3. Dropping 10 vol. hydrogen peroxide on MnO_2 as catalyst	$2H_2O_2(l) \rightarrow 2H_2O(l) + O_2(g)$
4. Electrolysis of acidified water	Oxygen is obtained at the anode

Industrial preparation of oxygen is by fractional distillation of liquefied air.

Test for oxygen It will rekindle a glowing splint.

Properties of oxygen It is a colourless, odourless, neutral gas, slightly denser than air and slightly soluble in water. Oxygen will not burn (non-combustible) but it will allow things to burn in it (supporter of combustion). Oxygen is a very reactive element combining with metals to form basic oxides and with non-metals to form acidic oxides.

Uses of oxygen

1. In the L.D. process for the production of steel from pig iron.
2. For breathing apparatus.
3. In oxyacetylene welding.

An oxide is formed when oxygen combines with an element to form a compound, e.g. calcium oxide, nitrogen dioxide, hydrogen oxide (water).

A basic oxide is a metallic oxide which reacts with an acid to produce a salt and water only; if it is soluble in water it forms an alkaline solution, e.g.

$$CaO(s) + 2HCl(aq) \rightarrow CaCl_2(aq) + H_2O(l)$$
$$CaO(s) + H_2O(l) \rightarrow Ca(OH)_2(aq)$$

Other examples are CuO, MgO, Na_2O, K_2O.

An acidic oxide is a non-metallic oxide which combines with the elements of water to produce an acid, e.g.

$$CO_2(g) + H_2O(l) \rightarrow H_2CO_3(aq)$$

Other examples are SO_2, SO_3, SiO_2.

An amphoteric oxide is a metallic oxide which shows both acidic and basic properties, e.g. ZnO, Al_2O_3.

Basic $\quad ZnO(s) + H_2SO_4(aq) \rightarrow ZnSO_4(aq) + H_2O(l)$
Acidic $\quad ZnO(s) + 2NaOH(aq) + H_2O(l) \rightarrow Na_2Zn(OH)_4(aq)$

A neutral oxide is a non-metallic oxide which shows neither basic nor acidic properties, e.g. NO, CO, H_2O.

A peroxide is an oxide which contains more oxygen than the corresponding basic oxide. All give hydrogen peroxide with dilute acids.

$$Na_2O_2(s) + H_2SO_4(aq) \rightarrow H_2O_2(aq) + Na_2SO_4(aq)$$

Properties of hydrogen peroxide

Hydrogen peroxide, H_2O_2, is a colourless syrupy liquid, usually used in dilute aqueous solution.

Heating or with MnO_2 as catalyst	Decomposes with the liberation of oxygen $2H_2O_2(aq) \rightarrow 2H_2O(l) + O_2(g)$
As an oxidizing agent	In many reactions H_2O_2 acts as an oxidizing agent, e.g. $PbS(s) + 4H_2O_2(aq) \rightarrow PbSO_4(s) + 4H_2O(l)$
As a reducing agent	Hydrogen peroxide behaves as a reducing agent toward certain compounds, e.g. $Ag_2O(s) + H_2O_2(aq) \rightarrow 2Ag(s) + H_2O(l) + O_2(g)$

Ozone is a colourless gas at ordinary temperatures and pressures. It is extremely poisonous and is a powerful oxidizing agent, e.g.

$$PbS(s) + 4O_3(g) \rightarrow PbSO_4(s) + 4O_2(g)$$

Because of its oxidizing action it is often used in high dilution for ventilating 'enclosed areas'.

Composition of air Air is composed of 78 per cent nitrogen, 21 per cent oxygen, 1 per cent inert gases, 0.03 per cent carbon dioxide together with variable amounts of water vapour and impurities.

Evidence for air being a mixture

1. Composition of air is almost constant over the earth's surface.
2. Air can be separated into its component parts quite easily by physical means, e.g. liquefaction followed by evaporation.
3. The properties of air are those which would be expected knowing its composition and are not those of a compound.
4. If the constituents of air are mixed in the correct proportions the resulting mixture resembles air in every way yet there is no evidence of chemical combination having taken place.

Allotropes of oxygen Oxygen (O_2) and ozone (O_3) are allotropes, the difference between them being one of molecular complexity.

Hydrogen

Isotopes of hydrogen Hydrogen has at least three isotopes – ordinary hydrogen, $_1^1H$, deuterium, $_1^2D$, and tritium, $_1^3T$.

Laboratory preparation of hydrogen

1. Treating zinc, iron or magnesium with dilute hydrochloric acid or dilute sulphuric acid.
$$Zn(s) + 2HCl(aq) \rightarrow ZnCl_2(aq) + H_2(g)$$
2. Action of steam on magnesium, aluminium or iron.
$$Mg(s) + H_2O(g) \rightarrow MgO(s) + H_2(g)$$
3. Electrolysis of acidified water. (H_2 obtained at cathode.)

Industrial preparation of hydrogen

1. From hydrocarbons, e.g. passing a mixture of methane and steam over a nickel catalyst.
2. By electrolysis. Hydrogen is obtained as a by-product in the manufacture of chlorine by the electrolysis of sodium chloride solution (see p. 48).

Properties of hydrogen

It is a colourless gas, almost insoluble in water and far less dense than air.

Combustion	Burns with a blue flame $2H_2(g) + O_2(g) \rightarrow 2H_2O(g)$
With sulphur	$H_2(g) + S(s) \rightarrow H_2S(g)$
As a reducing agent	Hydrogen is a powerful reducing agent, e.g. heat $CuO(s) + H_2(g) \rightarrow Cu(s) + H_2O(l)$

Test for hydrogen A mixture of air and hydrogen explodes when ignited.

Uses of hydrogen
1. In the synthesis of ammonia in the Haber process (p. 77).
2. In the hardening of oils to make margarine.
3. In the synthesis of hydrochloric acid and many organic compounds.
4. In the oxyhydrogen flame for welding and cutting steel.
5. In conversion of coal to synthetic petrol.

Water

Properties of water
1. It is a neutral oxide.

2. It reacts with metals high in the activity series to form hydrogen, e.g.

$$2Na(s) + 2H_2O(l) \rightarrow 2NaOH(aq) + H_2(g) \quad \text{(cold water)}$$
$$3Fe(s) + 4H_2O(g) \rightarrow Fe_3O_4(aq) + 4H_2(g) \quad \text{(steam)}$$

3. It forms acids with acid anhydrides.
$$SO_3(g) + H_2O(l) \rightarrow H_2SO_4(aq)$$

4. It forms bases with basic anhydrides.
$$NH_3(g) + H_2O(l) \rightarrow NH_4OH(aq)$$

5. It is a powerful solvent.

Test for water Water or liquids containing water turn anhydrous copper(II) sulphate blue, and/or cobalt chloride paper pink.

Water of crystallization is the water which is usually chemically combined with some substances when they crystallize from an aqueous solution. A **hydrated salt** is one which contains water of crystallization, e.g. washing soda ($Na_2CO_3.10H_2O$), magnesium sulphate ($MgSO_4.7H_2O$).
Deliquescence is the process which occurs when a substance absorbs moisture from the air, e.g. sodium hydroxide, NaOH.

A hygroscopic substance is a substance which absorbs moisture from the air without changing state, e.g. conc. sulphuric acid.

Efflorescence is the process which occurs when a substance loses its water of crystallization on exposure to air, e.g. washing soda ($Na_2CO_3.10H_2O$) eventually forms anhydrous sodium carbonate on prolonged exposure to air.

A dehydrating agent is an agent which will remove the elements of water from pure and perfectly dry compounds.

A drying agent is one which will remove water or water vapour from 'moist' substances, e.g.

Drying agent	Gas to be dried
Calcium chloride	Hydrogen
Calcium oxide	Ammonia
Concentrated sulphuric acid	Chlorine

Hard water is water which will not readily lather with soap.

Permanent hard water This type of hardness cannot be removed by boiling and is caused by the presence of the chlorides and/or the sulphates of calcium and magnesium.

Temporary hard water This type of hardness can be removed by boiling and is caused by the presence of dissolved hydrogen-carbonates of calcium and magnesium.

Removal of temporary hardness
The calcium or magnesium ions are removed from the water and converted into insoluble compounds.

1. *By boiling*. The soluble hydrogencarbonate decomposes to give the insoluble carbonate which is hence removed from the solution.
$$Ca(HCO_3)_2(aq) \rightarrow CaCO_3(s) + CO_2(g) + H_2O(l)$$

2. *By Clark's process*, which involves the addition of a calculated quantity of slaked lime.
$$Ca(HCO_3)_2(aq) + Ca(OH)_2(aq) \rightarrow 2CaCO_3(s) + 2H_2O(l)$$

Removal of temporary and permanent hardness
The calcium or magnesium ions are removed from the water by converting them into insoluble compounds.

1. *By distillation*. All the soluble salts are left behind.

2. *By adding washing soda* ($Na_2CO_3.10H_2O$). The soluble hydrogencarbonate is converted into an insoluble carbonate by double decomposition.

3. *By the Permutit process*. When hard water runs over Permutit which is sodium aluminium silicate, an ion exchange takes place, the permutit exchanging its Na^+ ions for the Ca^{2+} or Mg^{2+} ions in the water. Insoluble calcium or magnesium silicate is formed, and the water softened.

4. *By adding excess soap*. The soap (sodium stearate) reacts with the water to form insoluble calcium stearate, which usually floats on the top of the water as a scum.

$$CaSO_4(aq) + 2NaSt(aq) \rightarrow Na_2SO_4(aq) + CaSt_2(s) \text{ (St = Stearate)}$$

Carbon, Sulphur and Nitrogen

Carbon and its compounds

Allotropes of carbon Carbon exists in two allotropic forms –
diamond and graphite. Other forms of carbon are graphite.

Diamond is in the form of octohedral crystals. The crystal lattice
consists of a tetrahedral unit of five carbon atoms covalently
bonded and repeated throughout the structure. It is one of the
hardest substances known, used both in jewellery and industrially
in the manufacture of glass cutters and rock borers (Fig. 11a).

Graphite exists as opaque, black hexagonal crystals. It is a
macromolecule consisting of hexagonal units of parallel planes of
atoms. Bonding between atoms in the same plane is covalent,
between planes is by weak van der Waal's bond. It is a soft
substance, used extensively in the manufacture of lead pencils and
as a protective coating (Fig. 11b).

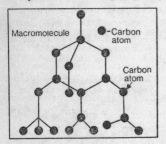

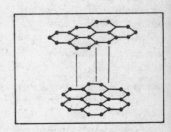

Figure 11a.   Diamond   *Figure 11b.   Graphite*

Laboratory preparation of carbon dioxide

1. Treat any carbonate or hydrogencarbonate with any dilute acid.
(There are a few exceptions.)
$$CaCO_3(s) + 2HCl(aq) \rightarrow CaCl_2(aq) + H_2O(l) + CO_2(g)$$

2. Heat any carbonate except those of sodium or potassium.

3. Heat any hydrogencarbonate. There are no exceptions.
$$2NaHCO_3(s) \rightarrow Na_2CO_3(s) + H_2O(l) + CO_2(g)$$

Collection of carbon dioxide is by downward delivery or the
upward displacement of air.

Test for carbon dioxide It turns limewater milky.

Properties of carbon dioxide
It is a colourless, odourless gas, easily solidified ($-80\,°C$).

Action of water	It is soluble in water producing a solution of the weak, unstable carbonic acid $H_2O(l) + CO_2(g) \rightleftharpoons H_2CO_3(aq)$
Action of alkalis	It dissolves to form carbonates and hydrogencarbonates $2NaOH(aq) + CO_2(g) \rightarrow Na_2CO_3(aq) + H_2O(l)$ $Na_2CO_3(aq) + H_2O(l) + CO_2(g) \rightarrow 2NaHCO_3(aq)$
Effect on burning magnesium	Carbon dioxide does not support combustion unless the substance is heated very strongly, e.g. $2Mg(s) + CO_2(g) \rightarrow 2MgO(s) + C(s)$

Uses of carbon dioxide
1. In the manufacture of mineral water.
2. Carbon dioxide is used as a refrigerant ('dry ice').
3. In fire extinguishers.
4. Used in baking powder.

Preparation of carbon monoxide By the action of heat on ethanedioic acid (oxalic acid) in the presence of concentrated sulphuric acid. The sulphuric acid dehydrates the oxalic acid to form a mixture of equal volumes of carbon monoxide and carbon dioxide

$$H_2C_2O_4(s) \rightarrow CO(g) + CO_2(g) + H_2O(l)$$

Carbon dioxide is removed by passing the mixture through two wash bottles containing potassium hydroxide solution.

Test for carbon monoxide It burns in air with a blue flame forming carbon dioxide, which turns limewater turbid.

Properties of carbon monoxide
It is a poisonous, colourless gas with practically no smell. It is a neutral oxide, insoluble in water which reacts with neither acids nor bases under normal circumstances.
Carbon monoxide is quite a strong reducing agent, e.g.

$$PbO(s) + CO(g) \rightarrow Pb(s) + CO_2(g)$$

Sulphur and its compounds

Allotropy of sulphur Sulphur exists in two well defined allotropic forms – rhombic sulphur and monoclinic sulphur. It also exists in two other varieties called plastic sulphur and amorphous sulphur which are not true allotropes.

Monoclinic (prismatic) sulphur Needle-like crystals in the form of long thin prisms. Obtained by melting sulphur then allowing it to cool; two holes are pierced in the crust, and excess sulphur is poured off. Monoclinic sulphur is left in the dish and under the crust. This is the most stable form above 96 °C.

Rhombic (octahedral) sulphur is prepared by dissolving powdered roll sulphur in carbon disulphide. Any undissolved sulphur is filtered off and the solution left to evaporate. Octahedral crystals of rhombic sulphur are formed. Rhombic sulphur is the most stable form below 96 °C.

Plastic sulphur is obtained by pouring boiling sulphur into water. It is not a true allotrope of sulphur.

Properties of sulphur

Combustion	Burns with a blue flame to form sulphur dioxide $S(s) + O_2(g) \rightarrow SO_2(g)$
Heating with metals	Combines with many metals to form sulphides, e.g. $2Cu(s) + S(s) \rightarrow Cu_2S(s)$
Action with hot concentrated sulphuric acid	Dilute acids do not attack sulphur. With the concentrated acid sulphur is oxidized to sulphur dioxide; sulphuric acid is reduced to sulphur dioxide. $S(s) + 2H_2SO_4(aq) \rightarrow 3SO_2(g) + 2H_2O(l)$
Action with hot concentrated nitric acid	The sulphur is oxidized to sulphuric acid $S(s) + 6HNO_3(aq) \rightarrow H_2SO_4(aq) + 6NO_2(g) + 2H_2O(l)$

Uses of sulphur
1. For the manufacture of sulphuric acid and calcium hydrogensulphite, which is used in the paper industry.
2. For the vulcanization of rubber.
3. For spraying hops and vines to prevent fungal growth.
4. In drugs, many of which contain sulphur.

Preparation of sulphur dioxide
By the action of hot concentrated sulphuric acid on any common metal, copper usually being chosen.
$$Cu(s) + 2H_2SO_4(l) \rightarrow CuSO_4(s) + 2H_2O(l) + SO_2(g)$$

Tests for sulphur dioxide
1. It has a very distinctive, irritating smell.
2. It turns filter paper soaked in potassium dichromate solution from orange to green.
3. It bleaches moist litmus paper.

Collection of sulphur dioxide is by upward displacement of air.

Properties of sulphur dioxide

It is a colourless gas with an irritating smell.

Action of water	Dissolves forming sulphurous acid. $SO_2(g) + H_2O(l) \rightarrow H_2SO_3(aq) \rightleftharpoons 2H^+(aq) + SO_3^{2-}(aq)$
Action of alkalis	Dissolves forming sulphites then hydrogen sulphites. $SO_2(g) + 2NaOH(aq) \rightarrow Na_2SO_3(aq) + H_2O(l)$ $Na_2SO_3(aq) + H_2O(l) + SO_2(g) \rightarrow 2NaHSO_3(aq)$
As a reducing agent	Sulphur dioxide is a very good reducing agent in the presence of water with which it forms sulphurous acid, e.g. it reduces iron(III) sulphate solution. $2Fe^{3+}(aq) + 2H_2O(l) + SO_2(g) \rightarrow$ $2Fe^{2+}(aq) + SO_4^{2-}(aq) + 4H^+(aq)$
As a bleaching agent	In the presence of water sulphur dioxide is a mild bleaching agent, the sulphurous acid removing oxygen from the dye.
As an oxidizing agent	It will allow magnesium to burn in it. $SO_2(g) + 2Mg(s) \rightarrow 2MgO(s) + S(s)$

Uses of sulphur dioxide

1. In the manufacture of sulphuric acid.
2. In the paper industry for bleaching wood pulp.
3. In the preservation of food-stuffs.

Sulphurous acid, H_2SO_3, is an unstable acid. It is dibasic forming two series of salts – sulphites and hydrogensulphites. It has all the reducing properties of sulphur dioxide.

Sulphur trioxide, SO_3, is a white crystalline hygroscopic solid.
Prepared by passing a mixture of dry sulphur dioxide and dry air or oxygen over heated platinized asbestos.

$$2SO_2(g) + O_2(g) \rightarrow 2SO_3(g)$$

With water it forms sulphuric acid.

Manufacture of sulphuric acid, H_2SO_4, is by the Contact process. Sulphur dioxide and air are passed over a heated catalyst of vanadium(V) oxide, V_2O_5, to form sulphur trioxide. The sulphur trioxide is then dissolved in concentrated sulphuric acid forming a fuming liquid, oleum, which is then diluted with water to give ordinary concentrated sulphuric acid.

$$2SO_2(g) + O_2(g) \rightleftharpoons 2SO_3(g)$$
$$H_2SO_4(aq) + SO_3(g) \rightarrow H_2S_2O_7(aq)$$
$$H_2S_2O_7(aq) + H_2O(l) \rightarrow 2H_2SO_4(aq)$$

Properties of sulphuric acid

It behaves in four ways:
1. as a dibasic acid (all strengths),
2. as a drying and dehydrating agent (when concentrated),
3. as an oxidizing agent (when hot and concentrated),
4. as a sulphate (all strengths).

Properties of sulphuric acid acting as an acid

It is a dense oily hygroscopic liquid.
1. Sulphuric acid is a strong dibasic acid producing two series of salts – sulphates and hydrogensulphates.
2. Some common metals displace hydrogen from the acid, e.g.
$$Fe(s) + 2H^+(aq) \rightarrow Fe^{2+}(aq) + H_2(g)$$

3. It liberates carbon dioxide from soluble carbonates, e.g.
$$Na_2CO_3(aq) + H_2SO_4(aq) \rightarrow Na_2SO_4(aq) + H_2O(l) + CO_2(g)$$

Properties of sulphuric acid acting as a drying or dehydrating agent.

1. It acts as a drying agent to most gases.
2. It removes the elements of water from formic acid and oxalic acid.
$$HCOOH(l) \rightarrow H_2O(l) + CO(g)$$
$$(COOH)_2 \rightarrow H_2O(l) + CO(g) + CO_2(g)$$

Concentrated sulphuric acid will remove the elements of water from blue copper(II) sulphate crystals which turn white.
$$\underset{\text{blue}}{CuSO_4 5H_2O(s)} \rightarrow \underset{\text{white}}{CuSO_4(s)} + 5H_2O(l)$$

Properties of sulphuric acid acting as an oxidizing agent

The acid splits up as follows: $H_2SO_4 - H_2O$, SO_2, O
1. It oxidizes carbon to carbon dioxide and sulphur to sulphur dioxide, e.g.
$$C(s) + 2H_2SO_4(aq) \rightarrow CO_2(g) + 2H_2O(l) + 2SO_2(g)$$

2. It oxidizes metals to oxides, then forms sulphates, e.g.
$$Cu(s) + 2H_2SO_4(aq) \rightarrow CuSO_4(aq) + 2H_2O(l) + SO_2(g)$$

Test for sulphate ion (sulphuric acid acting as a sulphate).
With barium chloride ($BaCl_2$) solution a white precipitate of barium sulphate is formed which is insoluble in dilute hydrochloric acid.
$$H_2SO_4(aq) + BaCl_2(aq) \rightarrow BaSO_4(s) + 2HCl(aq)$$

Uses of sulphuric acid

1. In the making of fertilizers, e.g. ammonium sulphate.
2. In the manufacture of artificial fibres and pigments for paint.
3. In the production of hydrochloric acid (salt gas) from salt.

Nitrogen and its compounds

Preparation of nitrogen, N$_2$

1. From the air by removing all other gases.

2. By heating ammonium nitrite solution.
$$NH_4NO_2(aq) \rightarrow N_2(g) + 2H_2O(l)$$

3. By passing ammonia over the hot oxide of lead, iron or copper.
$$2NH_3(g) + 3CuO(s) \rightarrow 3Cu(s) + 3H_2O(l) + N_2(g)$$

Properties of nitrogen Nitrogen is relatively inert but strongly heated magnesium burns in it to form magnesium nitride.
$$3Mg(s) + N_2(g) \rightarrow Mg_3N_2(s)$$

Nitrogen is used in the manufacture of ammonia and nitric acid.

Industrial preparation of ammonia is by passing nitrogen (from the air) and hydrogen (from water) at high pressure over a heated nickle catalyst, a process known as the *Haber* process.
$$N_2(g) + 3H_2(g) \rightleftharpoons 2NH_3(g)$$

Laboratory preparation of ammonia By heating any ammonium salt with an alkali, e.g.
$$Ca(OH)_2(s) + 2NH_4Cl(s) \rightarrow CaCl_2(s) + 2H_2O(l) + 2NH_3(g)$$

Test for ammonia

1. Smell. The gas has a characteristic choking smell.
2. Action with litmus. Ammonia turns moist red litmus paper blue.

Properties of ammonia

It is a colourless gas with a pungent smell turning red litmus paper blue. It does not burn in air or support combustion.

Action with water	It is very soluble in water producing a true base. $NH_3(g) + H_2O(l) \rightarrow NH_4OH (aq)$
Action with acids	Reacts to form salts (but not water), e.g. $2NH_3(g) + H_2SO_4(aq) \rightarrow (NH_4)_2SO_4(aq)$
Oxidation of ammonia to nitrogen monoxide	By passing the ammonia and oxygen over a heated platinum catalyst. $4NH_3(g) + 5O_2(g) \rightarrow 4NO(g) + 6H_2O(l)$
Oxidation of ammonia to nitrogen	By passing ammonia over a hot oxide of lead, iron or copper, e.g. $2NH_3(g) + 3CuO(s) \rightarrow 3Cu(s) + 3H_2O(l) + N_2(g)$
Action with chlorine	Ammonia is oxidized to nitrogen $8NH_3(g) + 3Cl_2 \rightarrow N_2(g) + 6NH_4Cl(s)$

Properties of ammonium salts

1. All ammonium salts are soluble in water.
2. All ammonium salts on heating with any base produce ammonia, e.g.

$$NH_4Cl(s) + NaOH(aq) \rightarrow NH_4OH(aq) + NaCl(aq)$$

3. On heating alone:

Ammonium chloride sublimes and dissociates

$$NH_4Cl(s) \rightleftharpoons NH_3(g) + HCl(g)$$

Ammonium nitrate melts and dinitrogen monoxide (N_2O) is evolved.

Ammonium nitrite gives off nitrogen when heated.

$$NH_4NO_2(s) \rightarrow N_2(g) + 2H_2O(l)$$

Preparation of dinitrogen oxide (nitrous oxide), N_2O, is

by double decomposition by heating a mixture of salts, e.g.

$$(NH_4)_2SO_4(s) + 2KNO_3(s) \rightarrow 2NH_4NO_3(s) + K_2SO_4(s)$$

On heating the ammonium nitrate melts and effervesces, dinitrogen oxide being liberated.

$$NH_4NO_3(l) \rightarrow N_2O(g) + 2H_2O(l)$$

Properties of dinitrogen oxide It is a colourless neutral gas,
which will rekindle a glowing splint. Used as an anaesthetic.

Preparation of nitrogen oxide

Nitrogen oxide is produced, mixed always with other oxides of nitrogen, by the action of nitric acid on most metals. Copper is usually chosen, the acid is fairly concentrated.

$$3Cu(s) + 8HNO_3(aq) \rightarrow 3Cu(NO_3)_2(aq) + 4H_2O(l) + 2NO(s)$$

Test for nitrogen oxide *By exposure to air* Reddish brown
fumes are produced on exposure to air due to oxidation of the gas.

$$2NO(g) + O_2(g) \rightarrow 2NO_2(g)$$

Action on iron(II) sulphate solution When iron(II) sulphate solution is poured into a gas jar containing nitrogen oxide, a dark brown or black coloration is obtained, caused by the compound $FeSO_4.NO$.

$$FeSO_4(aq) + NO(g) \rightarrow FeSO_4.NO(aq)$$

Properties of nitrogen oxide It is a colourless gas almost
insoluble in water. It supports the combustion of materials which are hot enough to decompose it and so liberate oxygen with which they may combine. For example, it supports the combustion of strongly burning magnesium and phosphorous.

$$P_4(s) + 10NO(g) \rightarrow P_4O_{10}(s) + 5N_2(g)$$
$$2Mg(s) + 2NO(g) \rightarrow 2MgO(s) + N_2(g)$$

Properties of nitrogen dioxide It is a reddish brown gas with a pungent irritating smell. *Prepared by* heating lead nitrate.

Action with water	When the brown gas is passed into water a pale blue solution results which is acidic. It contains the compounds nitrous and nitric acids $$2NO_2(g) + H_2O(l) \rightarrow HNO_2(aq) + HNO_3(aq)$$
Dissociation of nitrogen dioxide	On heating it dissociates to give an equilibrium mixture of N_2O_4 and NO_2 molecules. $$N_2O_4(g) \rightleftharpoons 2NO_2(g)$$

Industrial preparation of nitric acid By passing a mixture of ammonia and air over heated (700–800 °C) platinum catalyst.
$$4NH_3(g) + 5O_2(g) \rightarrow 4NO(g) + 6H_2O(l)$$

The nitrogen oxide is cooled and in excess air forms NO_2.
$$2NO(g) + O_2(g) \rightarrow 2NO_2(g)$$
The nitrogen dioxide is absorbed in hot water to give nitric acid.
$$2H_2O(l) + 4NO_2(g) + O_2(g) \rightarrow 4HNO_3(aq)$$

Laboratory preparation of nitric acid is by heating any nitrate (usually $NaNO_3$ or KNO_3) with conc. sulphuric acid.

$$NaNO_3(s) + H_2SO_4(aq) \xrightarrow[\text{heat}]{\text{gen'le}} NaHSO_4(aq) + HNO_3(aq)$$

$$NaNO_3(s) + NaHSO_4(aq) \xrightarrow[\text{heat}]{\text{strong}} Na_2SO_4(aq) + HNO_3(aq)$$

Properties of nitric acid It can react in two different ways:
1. as an acid (at all strengths);
2. as an oxidizing agent (best when concentrated).

Properties of nitric acid acting as an acid It gives salts with bases; it will liberate CO_2 from carbonates and hydrogencarbonates. Very dilute acid reacts with magnesium liberating H_2.

Properties of nitric acid acting as an oxidizing agent The acid may be regarded as splitting up thus: $2HNO_3 - H_2O$, $2NO_2$, O.

Action with carbon	Oxidizes carbon to carbon dioxide $$C(s) + 4HNO_3(aq) \rightarrow CO_2(g) + 2H_2O(l) + 4NO_2(g)$$
Action with sulphur dioxide and sulphite	Cold concentrated nitric acid oxidizes sulphites and sulphur dioxide to sulphates, e.g. $$H_2SO_3(aq) + 2HNO_3(aq) \rightarrow$$ $$H_2SO_4(aq) + H_2O(l) + 2NO_2(g)$$

Uses of nitric acid
1. In the manufacture of fertilizers and explosives.
2. In the preparation of substances from which dyes are made.

The Halogens and their Compounds

Industrial preparation of chlorine is by the electrolysis of sodium chloride solution; the other product is sodium hydroxide.

Laboratory preparation of chlorine

1. Oxidation of conc. hydrochloric acid with any oxidizing agent, e.g. $MnO_2(s) + 4HCl(aq) \rightarrow MnCl_2(aq) + 2H_2O(l) + Cl_2(g)$

2. Treatment of any chloride with manganese(IV) oxide and concentrated sulphuric acid.

$MnO_2(s) + 4NaCl(s) + 4H_2SO_4(aq) \rightarrow$
$\qquad 4NaHSO_4(aq) + 2H_2O(l) + MnCl_2(aq) + Cl_2(g)$

3. Treatment of bleaching powder with any acid, e.g.

$CaOCl_2(s) + 2HNO_3(aq) \rightarrow Ca(NO_3)_2(aq) + H_2O(l) + Cl_2(g)$

Properties of chlorine

Chlorine is a greenish-yellow gas with a suffocating smell.

Action of water	Dissolves producing hydrochloric acid and hypochlorous acid (chlorine water).
As an oxidizing (bleaching) agent	Chlorine is a very strong oxidizing agent; in sunlight, it combines explosively with hydrogen. $H_2(g) + Cl_2(g) \rightarrow 2HCl(g)$
With metals	Combines readily with some metals, e.g. $Mg(s) + Cl_2(g) \rightarrow MgCl_2(s)$
Action with phosphorous	Yellow phosphorous ignites in chlorine, e.g. $2P(s) + 5Cl_2(g) \rightarrow 2PCl_5(s)$
Action with bromide and iodide	It displaces bromine from bromides and iodine from iodides, e.g. $2KBr(aq) + Cl_2(g) \rightarrow 2KCl(aq) + Br_2(g)$
Action of cold dilute alkali solution	Dissolves to form a solution of the chloride and hypochlorite $Cl_2(g) + 2KOH(aq) \rightarrow KOCl(aq) + KCl(aq) + H_2O(l)$
Action of hot concentrated alkali	A mixture of potassium chloride and potassium chlorate is formed. $6KOH(aq) + 3Cl_2(g) \rightarrow$ $\qquad KClO_3(aq) + 5KCl(aq) + 3H_2O(l)$

Tests for chlorine

1. It is a greenish-yellow gas, with a characteristic smell.
2. It turns litmus paper red and then bleaches it.
3. It displaces iodine from potassium iodide solution, which turns starch iodine paper blue.

Bleaching powder, $CaOCl_2.H_2O$, is prepared by passing chlorine for some considerable time over solid slaked lime.

$$Ca(OH)_2(s) + Cl_2(g) \rightarrow CaOCl_2.H_2O(s)$$

Uses of chlorine

1. Extensively used as a bleaching agent.
2. In the manufacture of many organic chemicals, e.g. CCl_4.
3. To sterilize water both for domestic and industrial use.

Bromine, Br_2, is a heavy red volatile liquid with a choking irritating smell. It is prepared by the addition of concentrated sulphuric acid to an intimate mixture of potassium bromide and manganese(IV) oxide (analogous to chlorine). It is very similar to chlorine in its reactions though less vigorous.

Iodine, I, is a shiny black solid which sublimes when heated rapidly. It is soluble in potassium iodide solution due to the formation of the compound KI_3 and will also dissolve in ethanol, ether, carbon disulphide and trichloromethane.

Iodine does not bleach, is a mild oxidizing agent and will combine readily with metals to form iodides. In general its properties are similar to those of chlorine but less vigorous. Iodine is used as an antiseptic and in the treatment of goitre.

The order of reactivity of the halogens is fluorine > chlorine > bromine > iodine.

Preparation of hydrogen chloride (hydrogen acid), HCl

1. Burning hydrogen in chlorine
$$H_2(g) + Cl_2(g) \rightarrow 2HCl(g)$$

2. Heating a chloride with concentrated sulphuric acid, e.g.
$$NaCl(s) + H_2SO_4(aq) \rightarrow NaHSO_4(aq) + HCl(aq)$$

Tests for hydrogen chloride

1. It fumes in moist air.
2. It turns moist blue litmus red.
3. It forms dense white fumes with an ammonia bottle stopper.
4. It produces a white precipitate with silver nitrate solution.

Properties of hydrogen chloride

It is a colourless gas with a sharp taste and smell. It fumes in moist air and is soluble in water giving an acid solution.

Action with bases	Neutralizes bases to form a salt and water, e.g. $NaOH(aq) + HCl(aq) \rightarrow NaCl(aq) + H_2O(l)$
Action with certain metals	Reacts with, e.g., Mg, Zn, Fe liberating hydrogen $Zn(s) + 2HCl(aq) \rightarrow ZnCl_2(aq) + H_2(g)$ $Zn(s) + 2H^+(aq) \rightarrow Zn^{2+}(aq) + H_2(g)$
Action with carbonates	Liberates carbon dioxide $2HCl(aq) + Na_2CO_3(aq) \rightarrow$ $\qquad\qquad 2NaCl(aq) + CO_2(g) + H_2O(l)$ $2H^+(aq) + CO_3{}^{2-}(aq) \rightarrow CO_2(g) + H_2O(l)$

Tests for the halogens

Test. Addition of a few drops of silver nitrate solution, then excess ammonium hydroxide to a solution of the halogen.

Chloride	Bromide	Iodide
White precipitate of silver chloride readily soluble in excess ammonium hydroxide	Pale yellow precipitate of silver bromide slightly soluble in excess ammonium hydroxide	Primrose-yellow precipitate insoluble in ammonium hydroxide

Test. Addition of a few drops of the concentrated sulphuric acid to the solid halogen.

Chloride	Bromide	Iodide
Fumes of hydrogen chloride formed	Dark red droplets of bromine are formed and a reddish brown vapour evolved	Iodine vapour evolved

Organic Chemistry

Organic chemistry is the chemistry of the compounds of carbon (with the exception of carbon itself and simple compounds such as carbon dioxide and carbonates) in combination with at least one other element, e.g. hydrogen, oxygen, chlorine, nitrogen. Carbon is a remarkable element in that it is able to form very long chains of its atoms and also rings of atoms.

Aliphatic compounds are compounds which contain only a straight or branched chain of carbon atoms.

Aromatic compounds are compounds which contain a benzene ring as part of their structure. In addition they may also contain a straight or branched chain of carbon atoms.

A homologous series is a set of organic compounds which possess the following characteristics:

1. All members can be represented by a general molecular formula.
2. The molecular formula of each member differs from the next by $-CH_2$, e.g. the first three members of the alkane series are CH_4, C_2H_6 and C_3H_8.
3. All members possess similar chemical properties.
4. The physical properties of the members change gradually along the series in the direction of increasing molecular weight.
5. General methods of preparation exist which may be applied to any member of the series.

Examples of homologous series

Name of series	General molecular formula	Example
Alkanes	C_nH_{2n+2}	C_2H_6, ethane
Alkenes	C_nH_{2n}	C_2H_4, ethene
Alkynes	C_nH_{2n-2}	C_2H_2, ethyne
Alcohols	$C_nH_{2n+1}OH$	C_2H_5OH, ethanol
Carboxylic acids	$C_nH_{2n+1}COOH$	CH_3COOH, ethanoic acid
Esters	$C_nH_{2n+1}COOC_nH_{2n'+1}$	$CH_3COOC_2H_5$, ethyl ethanoate
Amines	$C_nH_{2n+1}NH_2$	CH_3NH_2, methylamine

A homologue is a member of a homologous series, e.g. butane, C_4H_{10}, is a member of the alkanes.

A saturated compound is an organic compound which reacts by substitution, i.e. it contains no spare bonds, e.g. the alkanes are saturated compounds.

An unsaturated compound is an organic compound which reacts by addition, i.e. it contains spare bonds. An unsaturated compound always contains at least one carbon to carbon double bond or one carbon to carbon triple bond, e.g. ethylene, $H_2C{=}CH_2$, ethyne, $HC{\equiv}CH$.

Substitution reactions are reactions in which one or more atoms of the organic compound are replaced by the same number of atoms of the reagent, e.g.

$$C_2H_6(g) + Cl_2(g) \rightarrow C_2H_5Cl(g) + HCl(g)$$

Addition reactions are reactions in which the molecule of a reagent combines with a molecule of the organic compound to form a new compound which contains all the atoms of the reacting organic compound, e.g.

$$CH_2{=}CH_2(g) + HBr(g) \rightarrow CH_3{-}CH_2Br(g)$$

Catalytic hydrogenation is the addition of hydrogen to a substance in the presence of a catalyst. Important examples are hydrogenation of fats and oils and napthalene, e.g.

$$H_2C{=}CH_2(g) + H_2(g) \rightarrow CH_3CH_3(g) \quad (\text{or } C_2H_6)$$

Hydrocarbons are compounds which contain hydrogen and carbon and no other element, e.g. methane CH_4, ethane C_2H_6 and benzene C_6H_6. The hydrocarbons are classified into several types according to their structure. Alkanes, alkenes and alkynes are all classes of hydrocarbon.

The alkanes are a homologous series of hydrocarbons with the general molecular formula C_nH_{2n+2}. They are saturated compounds which react by substitution of the hydrogen atoms. The first three members of the series are methane, CH_4, ethane, C_2H_6, and propane, C_3H_8.
The alkanes are a rather inert group giving only two reactions except under extreme conditions. They burn in air to give carbon dioxide and water and they are easily chlorinated in sunlight with the hydrogen atoms being substituted by chlorine atoms.

Isomerization is the occurrence when two or more compounds have the same molecular formulae but different structural formulae (i.e. different molecular structures).

Isomers are compounds which have the same molecular formulae but different structural formulae.

84

Isomers of molecular formula C_4H_{10}

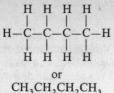

$$H-\overset{\displaystyle H}{\underset{\displaystyle H}{\overset{|}{\underset{|}{C}}}}-\overset{\displaystyle H}{\underset{\displaystyle H}{\overset{|}{\underset{|}{C}}}}-\overset{\displaystyle H}{\underset{\displaystyle H}{\overset{|}{\underset{|}{C}}}}-\overset{\displaystyle H}{\underset{\displaystyle H}{\overset{|}{\underset{|}{C}}}}-H$$

or

$CH_3CH_2CH_2CH_3$
butane

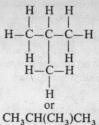

or

$CH_3CH(CH_3)CH_3$
2-methylpropane

Isomers of molecular formula C_2H_6O. There are two isomers – ethanol, structural formula CH_3CH_2OH and dimethyl ether, structural formula CH_3OCH_3. Both exhibit very different physical and chemical properties.

Petroleum is a mixture of paraffins which are separated into several fractions by fractional distillation. Petrol is obtained by redistillation of the naphtha fraction. Many products are obtained by breaking down the large molecules of the fractions into smaller molecules by a process of catalytic cracking.

Catalytic cracking is the breaking down of large complex molecules into smaller molecules with the aid of a catalyst. It is used extensively in the petroleum industry.

The alkenes are an homologous series of hydrocarbons with the general molecular formulae C_nH_{2n}. They are unsaturated compounds which contain at least one carbon to carbon double bond. They therefore act by addition across the double bond. The first two members are ethene, C_2H_4, structural formula $H_2C=CH_2$ and propene, C_3H_6, structural formula $H_2C=CHCH_3$.
The alkenes are a fairly reactive group of compounds reacting with for example chlorine, hydrogen iodide, concentrated sulphuric acid, hydrogen to form addition products.

Polymerization is the combination of two or more molecules of the same compound to form a more complex molecule with no gain or loss in material, i.e.

$$nX \longrightarrow X_n$$

A monomer is the original compound which polymerizes to form the polymer.

A polymer is a complex molecule which is built up by the addition of small molecules called monomers

Polyethene (polythene) is an addition polymer formed by the addition of about one thousand ethene molecules.

$$3n(CH_2{=}CH_2) \rightarrow (-CH_2-CH_2-CH_2-CH_2-CH_2-CH_2-)$$

The alkynes are a homologous series of hydrocarbons with the general molecular formula C_nH_{2n-2}. They are unsaturated compounds containing a carbon to carbon triple bond and hence react by the alkyl group from the alcohol. They may be hydrolyzed by C_2H_2, $HC{\equiv}CH$.

The acetylides are metallic derivatives of ethyne (acetylene). The two hydrogen atoms are replaced by two metal atoms, e.g. copper(I) acetylide, Cu_2C_2, structural formula $CuC{\equiv}CCu$.

The alcohols are a homologous series with the general molecular formula $C_nH_{2n+1}OH$. All the alcohols contain the characteristic hydroxyl group $-OH$. The first three members of the series are methanol, CH_3OH, ethanol, C_2H_5OH, and propanol, C_3H_7OH. They are a fairly reactive series. They (i) burn in air to form carbon dioxide and oxygen; (ii) they can be oxidized to the corresponding acid; (iii) being alcohols they form esters with an acid.

Fermentation is the slow decomposition of organic substances induced by micro-organisms or by enzymes. The reaction is usually highly exothermic. For example see Degradation below.

Degradation is the breaking down of a complex substance into several simpler substances. An example of degradation is the breaking down of starch by fermentation into alcohol and carbon dioxide. Starch (in the form of, for example, potatoes) is hydrolyzed by treating it with malt, which contains the enzyme diastase.

$$2C_6H_{10}O_5(aq) + H_2O(l) \rightarrow C_{12}H_{22}O_{11}(aq) \quad \text{maltose}$$

Maltose is hydrolyzed to glucose by the addition of yeast which contains the enzyme maltase.

$$C_{12}H_{22}O_{11}(aq) + H_2O(l) \rightarrow 2C_6H_{12}O_6(aq)$$

Another enzyme of yeast catalyzes the decomposition of glucose to ethanol and carbon dioxide.

$$C_6H_{12}O_6(aq) \rightarrow 2C_2H_5OH(aq) + 2CO_2(g)$$

The carboxylic acids are a homologous series with the general molecular formula $C_nH_{2n+1}COOH$. All the acids contain the characteristic carboxyl group, $-COOH$. The first three members of the series are methanoic acid, $HCOOH$, ethanoic acid, CH_3COOH and propanoic acid, C_2H_5COOH. They are all weak acids, reacting with alcohols to form esters, with phosphorous chloride to form the acid chloride, with chlorine in sunlight to form halides.

The esters are a homologous series with the general molecular formula $C_nH_{2n+1}COOC_{n'}H_{2n'+1}$. The characteristic group of the series is $-COOR$ where R is an alkyl group. The esters are not a very reactive group. They are synthesized by heating a carboxylic acid and an alcohol using concentrated sulphuric acid as catalyst. For example, synthesis of ethyl ethanoate

$$CH_3COOH(aq) + C_2H_5OH(aq) \rightarrow CH_3COOC_2H_5(aq) + H_2O(l)$$

The ionizable hydrogen of the carboxyl group, $-COOH$, is replaced by the alkyl group from the alcohol. They may be hydrolyzed by dilute mineral acid or dilute caustic alkali to give the acid and alcohol from which they were derived. Esters usually have a pleasant fruity smell and are used as flavouring materials and in perfumes. Examples of esters are methyl ethanoate, CH_3COOCH_3, ethylpropanoate $C_2H_5COOC_2H_5$.

Terylene is a complex ester, a polyester, formed by heating the alcohol ethane–1, 2–diol (glycol), $C_2H_4(OH)_2$ and the acid benzene–1, 4–dicarboxylic acid, $C_6H_4(COOH)_2$. The acid and alcohol condense forming an ester, with the elimination of molecules of water. Because both reactants contain two functional groups, the process may be repeated many times.

Esterfication is the process of producing an ester by heating an organic acid RCOOH with an alcohol R'OH in the presence of a few drops of concentrated sulphuric acid as catalyst.

$$RCOOH + R'OH \rightarrow RCOOR' + H_2O$$

where R and R' are alkyl groups.

The amines are a homologous series with the general molecular formula $C_nH_{2n+1}NH_2$. The characteristic group of the series is the amino group $-NH_2$.

Polystyrene (polyphenylethene) is a synthetic polymer formed by the polymerization of styrene $C_6H_5.CH{=}CH_2$. The polymer has a linear structure and may be depolymerized by heating to 350 °C.

$$-CH_2-CH-CH_2-CH-CH_2-CH-CH_2-CH-$$
$$\quad\ \ \ \ C_6H_5 \qquad\ \ C_6H_5 \qquad\ \ C_6H_5 \qquad\ \ C_6H_5$$

Polystyrene is a very good electrical insulator, is water resistant and can be used in thermal insulation and packaging.

Nylon is a condensation polymer formed by the polymerization of hexane–1,6–dioic acid $COOH(CH_2)_4COOH$ and 1,6–diamino-hexane $NH_2(CH_2)_6NH_2$. The structure of nylon is:

$$-CO(CH_2)_4CO-NH(CH_2)_6NH-CO(CH_2)_4CO-$$

Summary of gas preparations

The acid is slowly added to the reagent in a flat-bottomed flask. Heat is not required. The gas is collected over water.

Gas	Reaction	Test
H_2	$Zn(s) + H_2SO_4(aq) \rightarrow ZnSO_4(aq) + H_2(g)$ dilute	Explodes when ignited in air.
H_2S	$FeS(s) + 2HCl(aq) \rightarrow FeCl_2(aq) + H_2S(g)$ fairly conc.	Blackens lead(II) acetate paper.
CO_2	$CaCO_3(s) + 2HCl(aq) \rightarrow$ dilute $CaCl_2(aq) + H_2O(l) + CO_2(g)$	Turns lime water turbid.
NO	$3Cu(s) + 8HNO_3(aq) \rightarrow$ fairly conc. $3Cu(NO_3)_2(aq) + 4H_2O(l) + 2NO(g)$	Forms brown fumes on exposure to air.
Cl_2	$2KMnO_4(aq) + 16HCl(aq) \rightarrow$ conc. $2KCl(aq) + 2MnCl_2(aq) + 8H_2O(l) + 5Cl_2(g)$	Bleaches damp litmus paper. (Collected over brine)

The acid is slowly added to the reagent contained in a round-bottomed flask, which is heated. The gas is passed through one or more wash bottles and collected by displacement of air.

Gas	Reaction	Test
CO	$H_2C_2O_4(s) - H_2O(l) \rightarrow CO(g) + CO_2(g)$ oxalic acid (concentrated sulphuric acid is used to remove the elements of water)	Burns with a blue flame to carbon dioxide. (Two wash bottles of caustic potash solution)
SO_2	$Cu(s) + 2H_2SO_4(aq) \rightarrow$ $CuSO_4(aq) + 2H_2O(l) + SO_2(g)$	Decolorizes potassium permanganate solution without precipitate of sulphur. (Concentrated sulphuric acid in wash bottle)

Gas	Reaction	Test
Cl_2	$MnO_2(s) + 4HCl(aq) \rightarrow$ conc. $\qquad MnCl_2(aq) + 2H_2O(l) + Cl_2(g)$	Bleaches damp litmus. (Water in first wash bottle, conc. H_2SO_4 in second)
HCl	$NaCl(s) + H_2SO_4(aq) \rightarrow NaHSO_4(aq) + HCl(g)$ conc. (Heat is not essential)	Forms white precipitate of AgCl with silver nitrate in nitric acid solution. (Concentrated sulphuric acid in wash bottle)

The reagent is heated in a hard round-bottomed flask and the gas collected over water.

Gas	Reaction	Test
O_2	$2KClO_3(s) \rightarrow 2KCl(s) + 3O_2(g)$	Rekindles a glowing splint; not soluble in water.
N_2	$2KNO_2(s) + (NH_4)_2SO_4(aq) \rightarrow$ ammonium nitrite solution $\qquad 2N_2(g) + 4H_2O(l) + K_2SO_4(aq)$	Inert gas. Gives negative test with splint and lime water.
N_2O	$2KNO_3(s) + (NH_4)_2SO_4(aq) \rightarrow$ ammonium nitrate solution $\qquad 2N_2O(g) + 4H_2O(l) + K_2SO_4(aq)$	Rekindles a glowing splint; soluble in water.

A Table of common and chemical names

Common names	Chemical names	Formula
anhydrite	calcium sulphate	$CaSO_4$
bauxite	aluminium oxide	$Al_2O_3.2H_2O$
brine	sodium chloride (salt solution)	$NaCl(aq)$
caustic potash	potassium hydroxide	KOH
caustic soda	sodium hydroxide	$NaOH$
Chile saltpetre	sodium nitrate	$NaNO_3$
dolomite	calcium carbonate magnesium carbonate	$CaCO_3.MgCO_3$
Epsom salts	magnesium sulphate	$MgSO_4.7H_2O$
fluorspar	calcium fluoride	CaF_2
galena	lead sulphide	PbS
gypsum	calcium sulphate	$CaSO_4.2H_2O$
haematite	iron(III) oxide	Fe_2O_3
iron pyrites	iron(IV) sulphide	FeS_2
limestone, chalk	calcium carbonate	$CaCO_3$
limewater	calcium hydroxide solution	$Ca(OH)_2(aq)$
litharge	lead(II) oxide	PbO
magnetite	tri-iron tetroxide	Fe_3O_4
marble, calcite	calcium carbonate	$CaCO_3$
quicklime	calcium oxide	CaO
salt gas	hydrogen chloride	HCl
slaked lime	calcium hydroxide	$Ca(OH)_2$
washing soda	sodium carbonate	$Na_2CO_3.10H_2O$
zinc blende	zinc sulphide	ZnS

Alphabetical listing of elements and symbols

Element	Symbol	Atomic number	Element	Symbol	Atomic number
Actinium	Ac	89	Mercury	Hg	80
Aluminium	Al	13	Molybdenum	Mo	42
Americium	Am	95	Neodymium	Nd	60
Antimony	Sb	51	Neon	Ne	10
Argon	Ar	18	Neptunium	Np	93
Arsenic	As	33	Nickel	Ni	28
Astatine	At	85	Niobium	Nb	41
Barium	Ba	56	Nitrogen	N	7
Berkelium	Bk	97	Nobelium	No	102
Beryllium	Be	4	Osmium	Os	76
Bismuth	Bi	83	Oxygen	O	8
Boron	B	5	Palladium	Pd	46
Bromine	Br	35	Phosphorus	P	15
Cadmium	Cd	48	Platinum	Pt	78
Caesium	Cs	55	Plutonium	Pu	94
Calcium	Ca	20	Polonium	Po	84
Californium	Cf	98	Potassium	K	19
Carbon	C	6	Praseodymium	Pr	59
Cerium	Ce	58	Promethium	Pm	61
Chlorine	Cl	17	Protactinium	Pa	91
Chromium	Cr	24	Radium	Ra	88
Cobalt	Co	27	Radon	Rn	86
Copper	Cu	29	Rhenium	Re	75
Curium	Cm	96	Rhodium	Rh	45
Dysprosium	Dy	66	Rubidium	Rb	37
Einsteinium	Es	99	Ruthenium	Ru	44
Erbium	Er	68	Samarium	Sm	62
Europium	Eu	63	Scandium	Sc	21
Fermium	Fm	100	Selenium	Se	34
Fluorine	F	9	Silicon	Si	14
Francium	Fr	87	Silver	Ag	47
Gadolinium	Gd	64	Sodium	Na	11
Gallium	Ga	31	Strontium	Sr	38
Germanium	Ge	32	Sulphur	S	16
Gold	Au	79	Tantalum	Ta	73
Hafnium	Hf	72	Technetium	Tc	43
Helium	He	2	Tellurium	Te	52
Holmium	Ho	67	Terbium	Tb	65
Hydrogen	H	1	Thallium	Tl	81
Indium	In	49	Thorium	Th	90
Iodine	I	53	Thulium	Tm	69
Iridium	Ir	77	Tin	Sn	50
Iron	Fe	26	Titanium	Ti	22
Krypton	Kr	36	Tungsten	W	74
Lanthanum	La	57	Uranium	U	92
Lawrencium	Lr	103	Vanadium	V	23
Lead	Pb	82	Xenon	Xe	54
Lithium	Li	3	Ytterbium	Yb	70
Lutetium	Lu	71	Yttrium	Y	39
Magnesium	Mg	12	Zinc	Zn	30
Manganese	Mn	25	Zirconium	Zr	40
Mendelevium	Md	101			

Periodic Tal

PERIOD	Group 1	Group 2							
1	H Hydrogen 1 (1)								
2	Li Lithium 3 (7)	Be Beryllium 4 (9)							
3	Na Sodium 11 (23)	Mg Magnesium 12 (24)							
4	K Potassium 19 (39)	Ca Calcium 20 (40)	Sc Scandium 21 (45)	Ti Titanium 22 (48)	V Vanadium 23 (51)	Cr Chromium 24 (52)	Mn Manganese 25 (55)	Fe Iron 26 (56)	Co Cobalt 27
5	Rb Rubidium 37 (85.5)	Sr Strontium 38 (88)	Y Yttrium 39 (89)	Zr Zirconium 40 (91)	Nb Niobium 41 (93)	Mo Molybdenum 42 (96)	Tc Technetium 43 (99)	Ru Ruthenium 44 (101)	Rh Rhodium 45
6	Cs Caesium 55 (133)	Ba Barium 56 (137)	∗ La Lanthanum 57 (139)	Hf Hafnium 72 (178.5)	Ta Tantalum 73 (181)	W Tungsten 74 (184)	Re Rhenium 75 (186)	Os Osmium 76 (190)	Ir Iridium 77
7	Fr Francium 87 (223)	Ra Radium 88 (226)	† Ac Actinium 89 (227)						

Lanthanide Series	∗ La Lanthanum 57 (139)	Ce Cerium 58 (140)	Pr Praseodymium 59 (141)	Nd Neodymium 60 (144)	Pm Promethium 61 (147)	Sm Samarium 62 (150)	Eu Europium 63
Actinide Series	† Ac Actinium 89 (227)	Th Thorium 90 (232)	Pa Protactinium 91 (231)	U Uranium 92 (238)	Np Neptunium 93 (237)	Pu Plutonium 94 (242)	Am Americium 95

Elements

	Group 3	Group 4	Group 5	Group 6	Group 7	Group 0
						4 He Helium 2
	11 B Boron 5	12 C Carbon 6	14 N Nitrogen 7	16 O Oxygen 8	19 F Fluorine 9	20 Ne Neon 10
	27 Al Aluminium 13	28 Si Silicon 14	31 P Phosphorus 15	32 S Sulphur 16	35.5 Cl Chlorine 17	40 Ar Argon 18

59 Ni Nickel 28	64 Cu Copper 29	65 Zn Zinc 30	70 Ga Gallium 31	73 Ge Germanium 32	75 As Arsenic 33	79 Se Selenium 34	80 Br Bromine 35	84 Kr Krypton 36
106 Pd Palladium 46	108 Ag Silver 47	112 Cd Cadmium 48	115 In Indium 49	119 Sn Tin 50	122 Sb Antimony 51	128 Te Tellurium 52	127 I Iodine 53	131 Xe Xenon 54
195 Pt Platinum 78	197 Au Gold 79	201 Hg Mercury 80	204 Tl Thallium 81	207 Pb Lead 82	209 Bi Bismuth 83	210 Po Polonium 84	210 At Astatine 85	222 Rn Radon 86

157 Gd Gadolinium 64	159 Tb Terbium 65	162.5 Dy Dysprosium 66	165 Ho Holmium 67	167 Er Erbium 68	169 Tm Thulium 69	173 Yb Ytterbium 70	175 Lu Lutetium 71
247 Cm Curium 96	247 Bk Berkelium 97	251 Cf Californium 98	254 Es Einsteinium 99	253 Fm Fermium 100	256 Md Mendelevium 101	254 No Nobelium 102	257 Lr Lawrencium 103

Index

Other study aids in the  series

KEY FACTS CARDS

Latin
Julius Caesar
New Testament
German
Macbeth
Geography Regional
English Comprehension
English Language
Economics
Elementary Mathematics
Algebra
Modern Mathematics

English History (1815–1939)
Chemistry
Physics
Biology
Geometry
Geography
French
Arithmetic &
    Trigonometry
General Science
Additional Mathematics
Technical Drawing

KEY FACTS COURSE COMPANIONS

Economics
Modern Mathematics
Algebra
Geometry
Arithmetic &
    Trigonometry
Additional Mathematics

Geography
French
Physics
Chemistry
English
Biology

KEY FACTS A-LEVEL BOOKS

Chemistry
Biology

Pure Mathematics
Physics

KEY FACTS PASSBOOKS

Modern Mathematics
English History
    (1815–1939)
Biology
Chemistry

Physics
Geography
French
English

KEY FACTS MODEL ANSWERS

Modern Mathematics
English History
    (1815–1939)
Biology
Chemistry

Physics
Geography
French
English

KEY FACTS REFERENCE LIBRARY

O-Level Traditional
    & Modern Mathematics

O-Level Biology
O-Level Physics
O-Level Chemistry